C0-EEQ-969

398.2 F
FELTON
MIKE FIN
THE KE

BURLINGTON TOWNSHIP HIGH SCHOOL LIBRARY

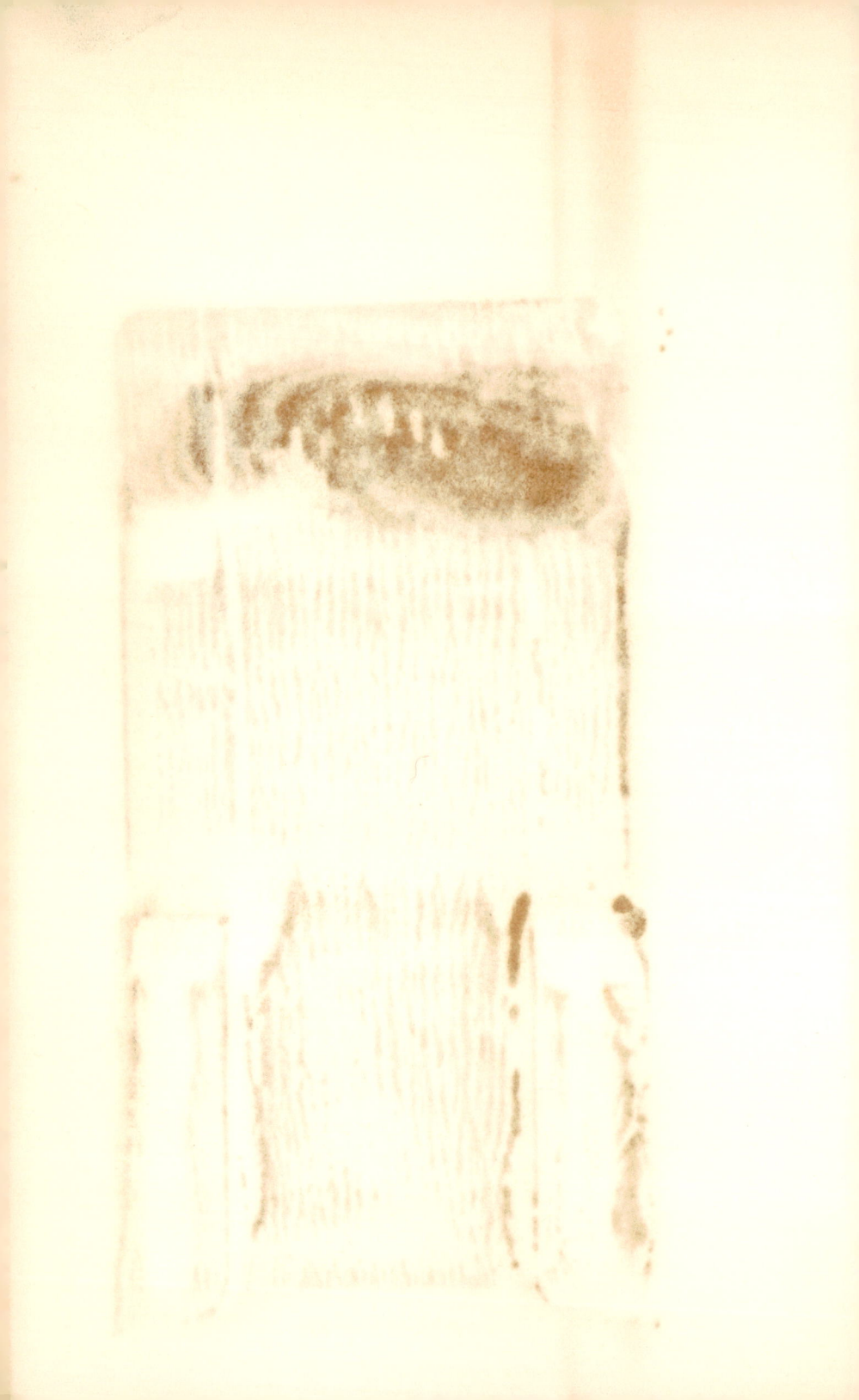

MIKE FINK
Best of the Keelboatmen

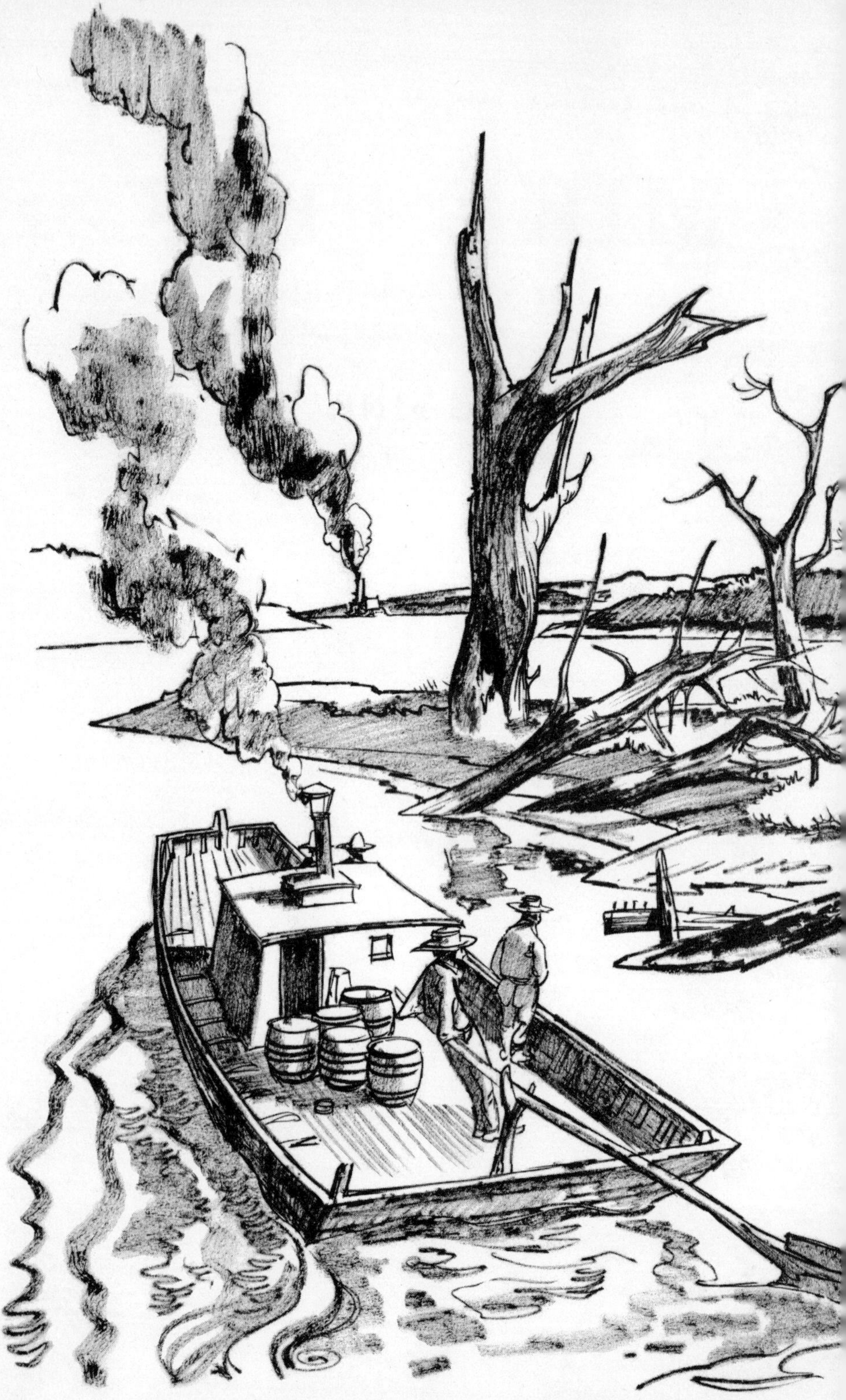

MIKE FINK

Best of the Keelboatmen

Being a Revealing and Trustworthy Account
of events in the Life of the
RENOWNED RIVERMAN,
Indian Scout, and Relentless Enemy of
divers and sundry outlaws

CONTAINING

Facts, Anecdotes, History, Legend,
and Folklore of the
UNIQUE AND JUSTLY FAMED HERO
including his experiences in his
Inimitable Craft, the *Lightfoot*

Taken from ancient, original sources by

Harold W. Felton

Tastefully amplified and illustrated by

ALDREN A. WATSON

DODD, MEAD & COMPANY
NEW YORK

© BY HAROLD W. FELTON, 1960

ALL RIGHTS RESERVED

NO PART OF THIS BOOK MAY BE REPRODUCED IN ANY FORM
WITHOUT PERMISSION IN WRITING FROM THE PUBLISHER
LIBRARY OF CONGRESS CATALOG CARD NUMBER: 60-6178
MANUFACTURED IN THE UNITED STATES OF AMERICA

Contents

	A Word about Mike Fink	7
1.	Fort Pitt on the Ohio	11
2.	A Scout Becomes a Boatman	24
3.	A Trip up Salt River	37
4.	On the River	47
5.	Screamers, Roarers and the Red Feather	57
6.	The *Lightfoot*	66
7.	"Dead Men Tell No Tales!"	76
8.	Mike Fink and Davy Crockett Shoot It Out	88
9.	The Disgraced Scalp Lock	96
10.	The Revenge of Proud Joe	104
11.	An Indian and a Deer	112
12.	Mike Fink Enjoys Lamb Stew	120
13.	Mike Fink in a Tight Place	132
14.	Mike Fink's Trip to Court	141
15.	To the Western Rivers	151

To my friend,
HENRY C. CLARK

A Word about Mike Fink

Was Mike Fink a real man? Is his story a true story? The answer is yes. This, and more.

The dates are correct as far as history books permit correctness. He was born at the birthplace of the Ohio River, near Pittsburgh. He worked on the rivers of the new west, and went to the still newer west with Ashley and there died of an ailment common in those days. Lead poisoning, brought on by a bullet in the head. Some of the stories about him are true, and some are truer still. Mike Fink was a legend and a myth in his own time. Folks told and wrote stories about him then, and have continued to do so ever since.

He was a man who excited imagination, the first requisite of a hero. The time he lived and the place he lived and worked may have something to do with it. Men were moving their families and possessions westward, over rough land without a road worthy of the name, to the rivers that would carry them still farther west. They were working their way from the Atlantic coast to the vast open spaces of the western regions. This was the frontier. There was a challenge around every bend. Imaginations soared.

Such men are entitled to think big and talk tall. They needed heroes and Mike Fink became one of them. Davy Crockett was another, and there were many more.

The story of Mike Fink is based on good solid fact, and is as true as fancy can make it. Everyone who tells a story about a hero adds something to it. If it is about a hero it must be that way. Heroes do not remain dull or static. They must grow. They must be truer than life, and larger.

I have read all the old tales I could find about Mike Fink and have fashioned them into this book. I was sorry not to be able to find a place for the one about Mike's stomach ache. The doctor told him the lining of his stomach had worn out. Must have been something he ate or drank, no doubt. Here was a problem, but Mike was equal to it. He ate a buffalo hide, hair and all. It proved to be indigestible, as he knew it would be, and it settled down after a time quite properly as a new stomach lining. It was durable. He never had a moment's distress after that.

In his day Mike's name was at times used by some mothers living along the rivers to frighten their children. "Be good or Mike Fink will get you," they said. I have

A Word about Mike Fink

not included the stories that gave rise to this side of the legendary Mike Fink.

Also, I have truthened up the tales where the truth seemed to be a little weak, and I have factualized them where the facts seemed to need bracing. Parson Weems in his *Life of Washington* gave us one of our most enduring and charming legends in this fashion. What would we be without the story of the hatchet and the cherry tree? Cotton Mather was a good man at this sort of thing, too. He braced up lots of facts.

Imagination has loosened tongues and pens for a long time. It has worked for many years on Mike Fink, as well as on most other heroes. So here he is. Mike Fink. As true as life and history and imagination can make him.

HAROLD W. FELTON

1. Fort Pitt on the Ohio

DAY busted the day Mike Fink was born. It didn't break that morning. It busted. Night didn't fade. It sort of snapped off and the sun came up with a jump. It was easy to see that something important happened that day. The important thing was that Mike Fink was born.

That day Mike Fink was born, the day the day busted, wasn't merely the dawn of a new day. It was the dawn of a new era. Great events were soon to occur. In the span of a lifetime, Mike Fink's lifetime, a wilderness would be tamed—almost. A nation would be born, and a nation would grow great and strong.

It was 1770 and the place was Fort Pitt. Across the river, and north of the Ohio, was Indian country. If a man went there it was a good idea to go with a rifle in one hand and the other one on top of his head if he wanted to be sure to keep his scalp.

The little frontier settlement lay in the triangle where the Monongahela River joined forces with the Allegheny. Where the Ohio River flooded into being and began its surge to the sea.

Mike Fink did what all boys did. He grew and went to school, sometimes, and he played, sometimes. He thrilled at the sound of the boatmen's horns as the flatboats passed. He helped with the garden. He cut down trees and grubbed out stumps and brush. And he pushed the wilderness back from the little cabin in the little clearing that was his home.

He learned to swim. He learned to hunt. He learned to shoot. He was an expert marksman before he was big enough to hold a long-barreled rifle out straight. He rested it on a stump or against a tree.

In his boyhood the War of the Revolution swirled through and around Pittsburgh, and Mike Fink spent his boyhood hearing tales of heroes and patriots, and seeing the men who were making history. Three rivers were before his door and his eyes. He saw the river traffic, born of the war, the movement of raiders, supplies and prisoners.

Mike earned his first money by shooting wolves for bounty. It was his experience with a wolf that made it clear that Mike was not made of the same stuff as other young men. He had boasted that he would kill a large, ferocious wolf that had been terrorizing the neighborhood. Mike said, "I aim to spiflicate him hull."

His chance came a few days later on a winter morning that was furiously cold. The monster, maddened by hunger, attacked him. He was unable to use his rifle, for the wolf gave him no warning. It sprang on him from behind and sought his jugular vein.

A quick twist put them face to face. Mike's fists struck against steel-like claws and teeth. He broke through the swirling, barbed attack. The beast fell back on his haunches. At the next attack, Mike fell back on the ground. In a flash the creature was upon him. In another flash the cruel jaws were making a death bite at him. In still another flash Mike gave him a terrible blow in the pit of the stomach. The wolf gasped, buckled up, and fell, defeated!

Mike was the best shot in Pittsburgh. The best shot in the western country. Most people knew it all along. But one day everyone found it out. That day there was a shooting match. The prizes were quarters of beef. Six "quarters." Two front quarters. Two hind quarters. The fifth quarter was the hide and tallow. And the sixth quarter was the leaden bullets in the tree that held the target.

The best shot won the first choice and Mike always won the choice for the first quarter. But that day he bought five chances. The boy shot against the best men in the West. When the shooting match was over Mike had won the five quarters of beef. And the sixth was his, too.

After that they called him "Bang All," and that

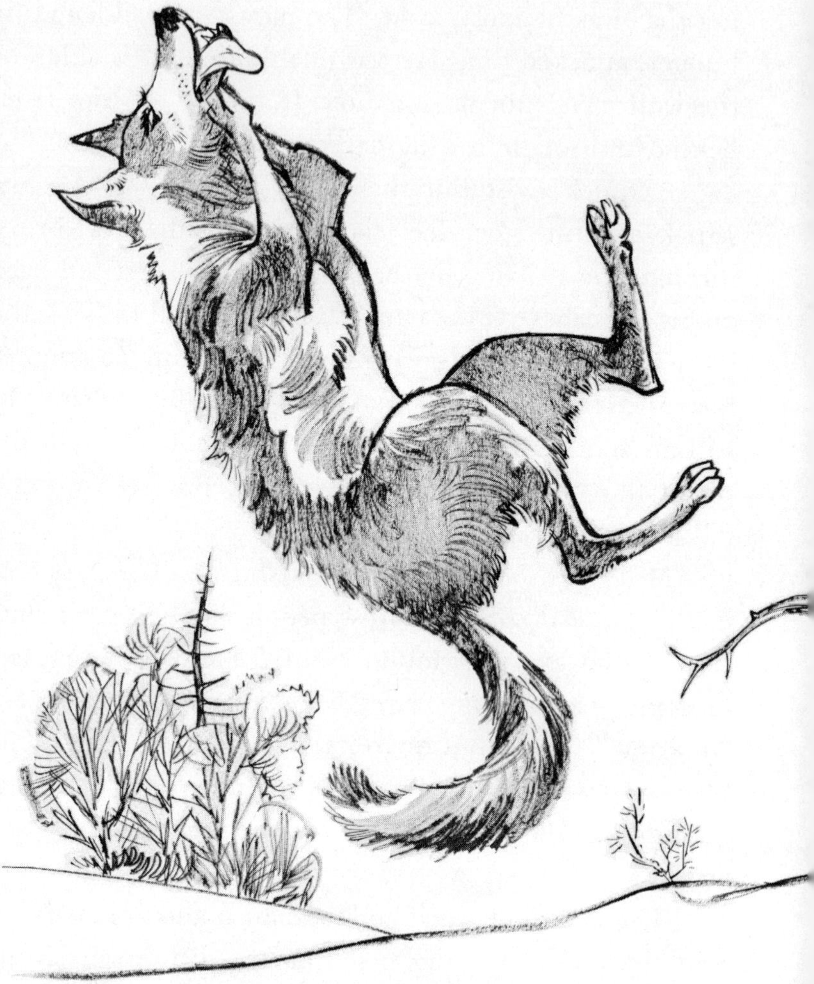

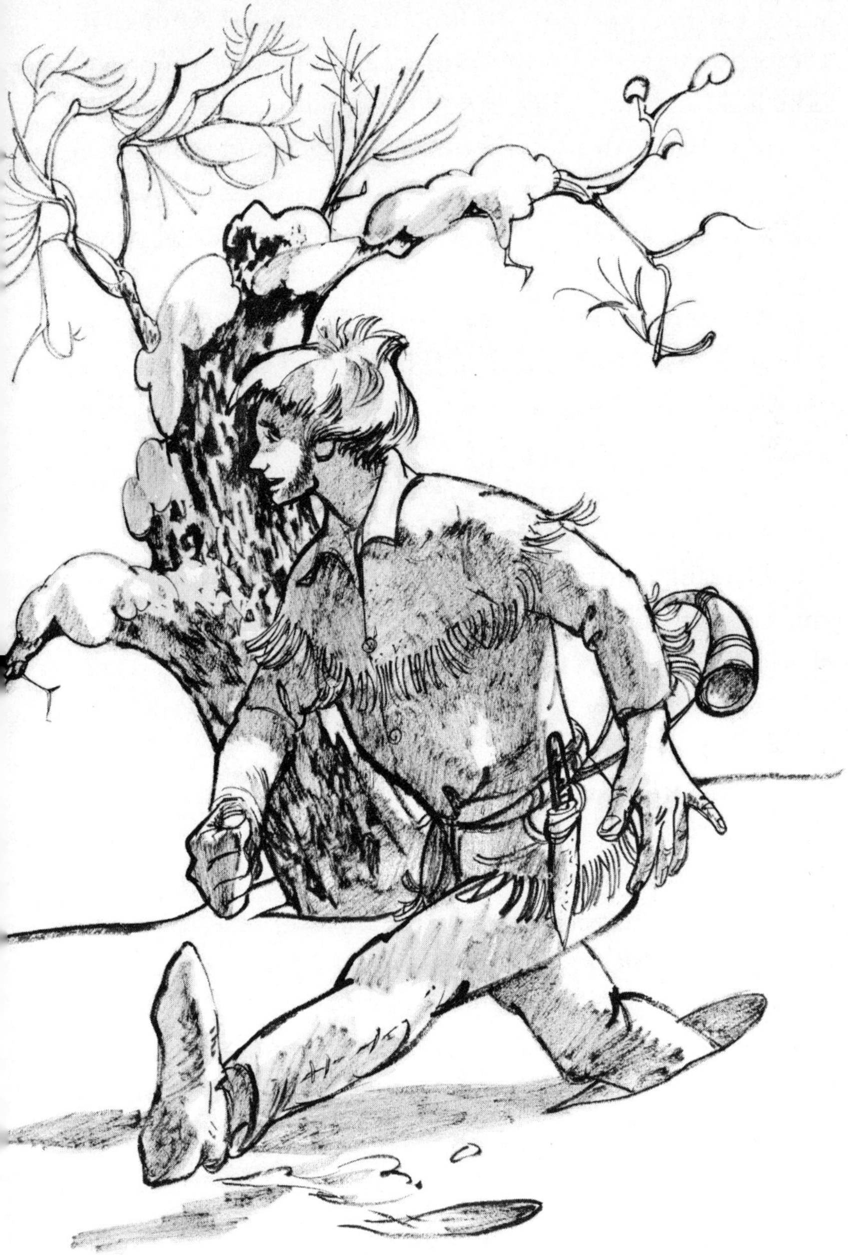

was the name they gave his long-barreled rifle. After that they always gave him the fifth quarter for *not* shooting. The hide and the tallow brought a good price.

But Bang All had other targets. They said that to see young Mike Fink shoot the heads of nails at sixty paces, and drive the nails into the wood was "one of the purtiest sights in the whole creation."

He could snuff out a candle flame with his rifle ball. When he was fifteen years old, he snuffed out the fifteen candles on his birthday cake with fifteen shots at fifty paces.

"It was a real enoblin' sight fer sore eyes," they said, when they saw him shoot a bird on the wing.

Barking squirrels was a favorite sport. Mike shot at the bark on the limb where the squirrel sat. It was the shattering bark that knocked the squirrel down. That way he got a whole squirrel, not one half-destroyed by a spreading rifle ball.

In shooting at a target, his bullets never made more than one hole. He piled them in, shot after shot, one bullet on top of another.

They sat around their cabin fires on the Western Frontier and talked about young Mike Fink.

"He's got an eye as keen as a sarpint."

"It's somethin' more'n real interstin' to see that rifle come up to his peepers, an' then git real solid, like a rock, an' then blaze away."

"His aim's plumb poison."

"He's as tough as hickory, and as long-winded as a nor'wester."

Fort Pitt on the Ohio

"He kin dodge a tomahawk flyin' at him."

"Mike Fink kin even dodge a bullet. I swar he kin."

"An' in the woods he's a caution. He travels faster than a hunted painter. Faster than a skeered wild cat in a thunder storm."

"You're goin' to hear of that young feller some day."

"Some day? Why, you hear of him all the time now."

Mike longed to go on the river and make a living there. But in those days there was very little river traffic. Small loads and short hauls for the most part. Portages around the falls and ripples.

He knew that some day he would go on the river. He would take a boat. A heavy boat to New Orleans. New Orleans! It was at the end of the rivers and Frenchmen lived there. He had heard about that city.

The year before Mike Fink was born Daniel Boone left his home on the Yadkin River "to wander through the wilderness of America in quest of the country of Kentucky."

The year Mike was born Daniel Boone throbbed with wonder, pride and amazement when he saw for the first time the great Ohio River.

Fort Pitt was growing fast. And why not? Wasn't it located at the end of two rivers and at the beginning of a third? The two, the Monongahela and the Allegheny, pierced the mountains back to West Virginia on the south, and New York on the north. The one, the Ohio, went forward to the new West and the South.

The rivers that met at Fort Pitt were a part of thousands of miles of rivers that touched unknown lands.

A lacework of rivers, of water roads, that spread far and wide over a new, unmapped wilderness.

Endless miles of rivers. Here, there, everywhere. They wound about. They tarried, and they rushed. They dropped slowly, or fast, and they grew large. And endlessly they touched the land. They fondled the prairies, and washed the forests. They brushed against the mountains, and rested in the swamps, and went around the deserts. The rivers nourished the land on which one day farms and towns would grow.

In the union of the Monongahela and the Allegheny, the Ohio was born big. It grew larger as other rivers fell in its embrace. From the north and from the south, other rivers wandered down to join the Ohio.

Then, at length, 1,100 miles from its birthplace, the Ohio swirled, in a turmoil of boils and eddies and whirlpools, into the fullness of the great Mississippi. Then, this endless flood surged south until at New Orleans, 1,000 miles still farther, the brown blood from the heart of the nation lost itself in the ocean and moved on to all the oceans of the world.

So the little settlement of Pittsburgh was tied by water ribbons, as strong and as enduring as eternity, to all of the great central West. The rivers were the first roads. On them the life of the nation flooded west. In those dangerous, fast-moving years, the westward march on the slow-moving rivers was in the hands of Mike Fink and the river boatmen.

Fort Pitt was beyond the edge of civilization. But civilization was coming, and it was coming fast.

Fort Pitt was in the middle of a war. War with the Indians and with the French. With the British and with the wilderness. Always war with the Indians and the untamed wilderness.

As people came in increasing numbers, the Indians and the wilderness were pushed back. But they didn't push easy. They fought, and they fought hard. Rewards were paid for scalps, but not for prisoners. An Indian scalp was worth as much as a panther skin. A white man's scalp was just as valuable.

Mike Fink was in the vanguard. In the front line from his birth to the end. But life was not complicated. The first and most important thing to do was to keep your hair on your head, and try not to stop a tomahawk with your skull. Beyond that it was not difficult. You could make your own soap, and salt. Of course you might have to travel a hundred miles or so to the salt lick. You could make your own clothes out of buckskin, after you shot the deer and tanned the skin. If you needed some cloth, you could make your own linsey, after you grew and harvested the flax and carded and spun and wove. You could make socks, rough, but warm, out of buffalo wool. You could eat well. Raise some hogs and butcher and salt the meat. Raise some corn and grind corn meal or make hominy. Hawg and hominy. Made a good meal. Naturally, there was always game to shoot.

In 1777 Mike Fink, a boy of seven years, throbbed with excitement. Captain George Gibson and Lieutenant William Linn returned after making a round trip to

New Orleans in freight-carrying boats. They brought back 156 kegs of badly needed gunpowder. The War of the Revolution went on.

In his lifetime Mike Fink saw the conquest of Kentucky, the beautiful land that was called "the dark and bloody ground." A land of fabulous hunting. Fought for by the Cherokees, the Creeks and the Chickasaws from the south, and the Algonquins and the Wyandots from the north, and by the white pioneers and hunters from the east. Kentucky, a land so beautiful that a preacher trying to describe heaven, called it "a Kentucky of a place."

Mike Fink saw the Ohio country settled by the New Englanders who sang as they struggled over the mountains and floated down the streams:

> When rambling o'er these mountains
>   And rocks where ivies grow
> Thick as the hairs upon your head
>   'Mongst which you cannot go;
> Great storms of snow, cold winds that blow,
>   We scarce can undergo;
> Says I, my boys, we'll leave this place
>   For the pleasant Ohio.
>
> Our precious friends that stay behind,
>   We're sorry now to leave;
> But if they'll stay and break their shins,
>   For them we'll never grieve;
> Adieu, my friends! Come on, my dears,
>   This journey we'll forego
> And settle Licking Creek,
>   In yonder O-hi-O.

In 1786 when Mike Fink was sixteen years old,

tomahawks and scalping knives were sold in the stores of Pittsburgh.

Mike Fink saw George Rogers Clark float down the Monongahela and the Ohio to the Falls of the Ohio in 1778, from whence, with a handful of men, he took Kaskaskia, Cahokia and Vincennes, and conquered Illinois.

Mike Fink saw his country's great growth with the Louisiana Purchase in 1803. He lived when Lewis and Clark went up the muddy Missouri in 1804 and returned two years later with tales of wonder. He knew at firsthand of the Burr conspiracy in the new West, when one who might have been a hero stumbled with feet of clay.

Mike Fink knew Daniel Boone and Davy Crockett. He knew the great Indian hunters, fighters and trappers. Lewis Wetzel who was captured by the Indians and escaped from them, and who killed them by the score. Kaspar Mansker whose gun was called "Nancy," and who was one of Boone's famous long hunters. He once killed so many deer, elk and buffalo that his party could not pack the hides back to camp.

Mike knew Simon Kenton, who could load his muzzle-loading rifle on the run. He could throw his own coonskin cap in the air and hit it with a ball from his long-barreled Kentucky rifle before it struck the ground.

He saw the boatmen fight with Andy Jackson in the Battle of New Orleans. He saw the furs and peltries come down the long, muddy Missouri River. And he knew the men who took them from the vast, new, western wilderness.

Mike became an Indian scout. He traveled through

the woods alone and scouted the territory around Pittsburgh. He wore pants, leggings, and a long hunting jacket of fringed buckskin, moccasins, and a coonskin cap. He carried a tomahawk and a knife sheathed in his belt. A shot bag and a powder horn hung from straps thrown over his shoulder. He carried his rifle, extra flints, a blanket, some salt, corn meal and jerky. So equipped, he would disappear into the woods for a week or a month. He lived on the country. When Indians were near and no shot could be fired, when the corn meal and the jerky were gone, he made a meal out of "belt soup." Easy and quick to prepare. Just tighten the belt another hole, and stick it out.

When Mike Fink was back in Pittsburgh, with all the comforts of home, he lived in a dirt-floored cabin. Cooking and eating utensils were few and were made of wood and pewter, except for the iron cooking pot. The food was hawg and hominy, and game. Mike Fink could always manage to get on the outside of another helping of hominy as long as it lasted.

He traveled noiselessly through the woods like a buckskin ghost. A moving, silent shadow in the silence and shadows of the forest. He fought Indians. He looked for signs of Indian unrest. He sought out Indian marauders and war parties. With other scouts, he fought Indians.

He turned an extra dollar now and then by a job on the river. When there was a chance, he hired out as a hand on a flatboat or a barge. Short jobs and short hauls. A load to Wheeling. Another to Limestone or Redstone.

Once he helped bring a load of pine planks to Pittsburgh from southwestern New York.

And when he paused and looked at the river, he saw that the local traffic was growing. The flatboats were getting bigger. The loads were getting larger. The trips were getting longer. To Marietta and Gallipolis and Cincinnati, and Louisville, where the Falls of the Ohio stopped the big flatboats.

Some day his chance would come! Some day Mike Fink would be a boatman! Some day he would go to New Orleans. New Orleans! Where people spoke French, and wore their Sunday clothes every day!

2. A Scout Becomes a Boatman

THE little church in Cross River just below Pittsburgh was full. Mike Fink, Indian scout, wandered in the door. He was young. Barely sixteen. The youngest Indian scout. And one of the best. A trapper and hunter as well, he had done a man's work for several years. He was well known there. The speaker paused when Mike entered, and then continued.

"That's about all there is to it. We owe the minister three years' salary."

A tall man with a black beard interrupted. "We owe him, an' we ought to pay him. But we hain't got no money. We got wheat an' corn an' hogs, but that hain't money. An' it hain't even worth no money. You cain't hardly even trade it fer powder an' lead an' salt. Not here, anyways."

"They need wheat in the East."

"They need flour everywhere but here."

The words came thick and fast. But there was no answer to the problem. There was plenty of grain, but no market for it.

Mike Fink spoke up. "Why don't you take the wheat to market?" he asked.

Some of the faces turned toward him. The tall man spoke. "It would cost more than six, mebby ten dollars a hundredweight to haul wheat from Pittsburgh to Philadelphia or Baltimore," he said.

"No," said Mike. "I mean take it the other way. Down the river."

In all their discussions, no one had mentioned that. It had never been done, so it couldn't be done.

But they hadn't had Mike Fink with them before. "In the war, Captain Gibson done it," he said.

"But he had soldiers to make the portages. You got to carry the freight around the falls an' the ripples. You cain't do that 'less you got a lot of men."

"There ain't no falls. Not real ones, anyways," replied Mike. "The biggest ones is at Louisville. I bin over 'em in a canoe lots of times. There ain't no reason why a loaded flatboat can't go over 'em if it ain't too wide and the gunwales is high enough."

"But nobody has ever done it. Not that I ever heard of, anyway."

"That don't mean it can't be done," said Mike.

"People go almost everywhere on the river. The only thing that ain't been done is that no one has ever took a load of flour all the way to New Orleans."

There was a murmur of question. Then argument. "We might at least try it," the tall man said at last. "If we put a load of wheat on a flatboat, it won't cost hardly nothin'."

"We got the lumber to build the boat. We got the wheat. They ain't nothin' else to do with it anyway."

"Yes, but who'll go?"

Who would go? The people turned to each other. Mike saw his chance.

"I'll do it," he said. "I'll take your flatboat to New Orleans." It was his chance to get on the river. Yes, it was dangerous. But he knew he could do it. Hadn't he taken on a wolf singlehanded? Hadn't he tangled with Indians? Just let him at the river!

"But, Mike, you're too young to make a trip like that."

"I'm old enough to be an Indian scout. An' a lot of men never do git old enough fer that." It was a shattering reply.

"I bin on the river a lot an' I'm as ambitious as a wildcat to git on her more. I'm as brash and tough as a new dog, an' I don't run from a fight. I bin walkin' tall into Indians an' all sorts of varmints. I figger I'll jest walk tall into that river, too!"

"I've known Mike fer a coon's age," Grandpaw Smiley said. "If anybody kin do it, he kin. I hain't got no fambly to take keer or. I hain't got no crops to put in.

I'll jest go along with Mike!"

"I'll go along, too." Everybody turned. It was Talbott. Big Talbott. A hunter from Kentucky.

"Me, too. I want to go!" Heads turned the other way. There was young Carpenter. A boy. Just big enough to lift and load a rifle. An orphan since an Indian raid late in the fall.

"Then," said Mike, "you're in the crew." He turned to the people. "If you want to try an' pay the parson in about the only way you can, the first thing we got to have is a flatboat. So let's git about it. I'm spilin' for a fight with them river snags. All I ask is half a chance and the odds against me."

Now there was a new spirit among them. The flatboat rapidly took shape. Barrels were made and flour was stowed away on the new craft.

The day came. "We wish you well. Whatever happens, come back safe and sound," the preacher said.

"We'll come back all right, but not till we see New Orleans," said Mike Fink.

It was March. The best time for down river travel. The ice had broken and water from the melting snow had brought the river to a high stage. Mike had worked on boats. He knew the dangers. Indians. Ice jams. Snags. Wooden islands. Whirlpools. Sawyers. Planters. Sand bars. Falls. Ripples. But he had never been a captain. Now he was. A patroon, a captain. With full responsibility for the safety of cargo, crew and craft. He grinned as he felt the rudder oar under his hand.

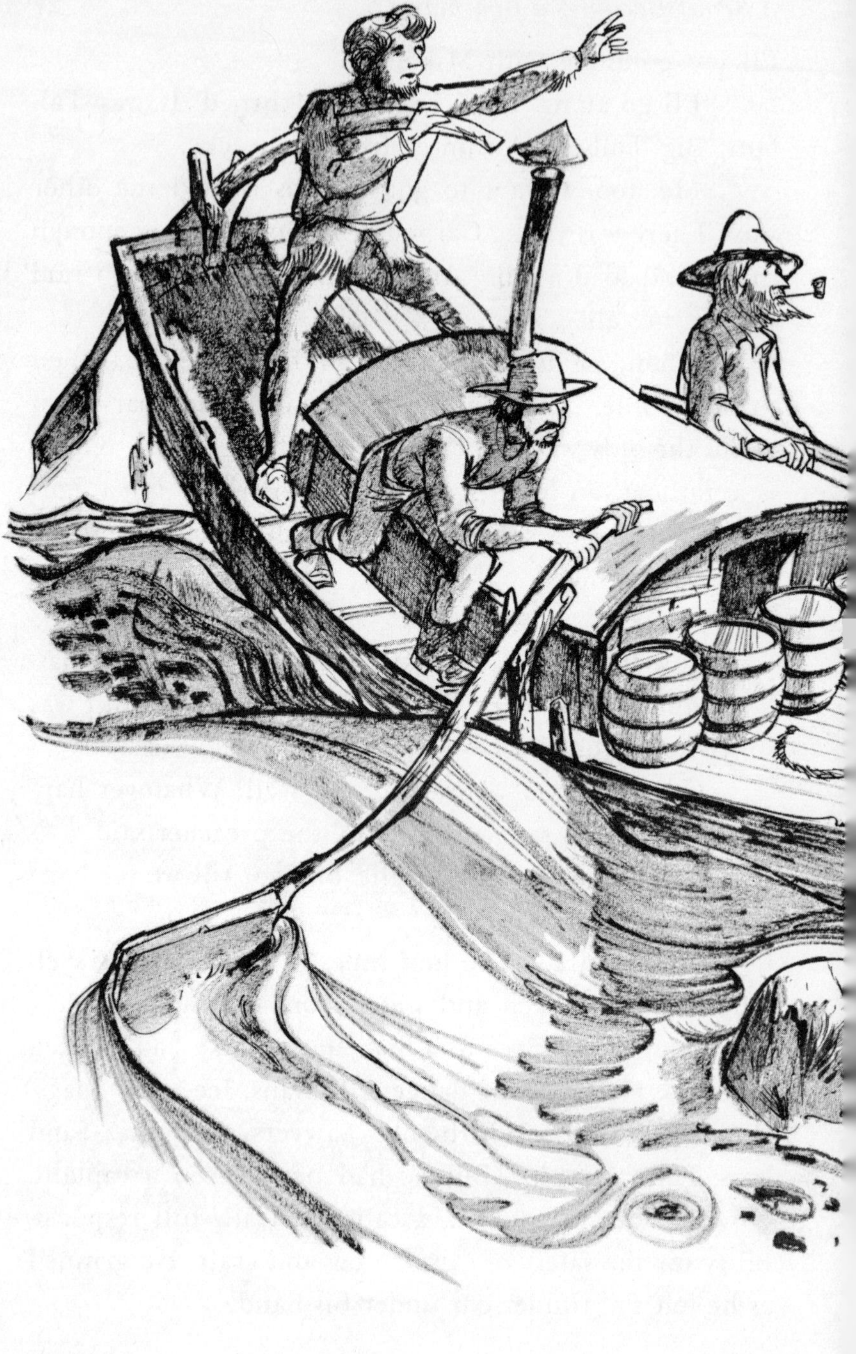

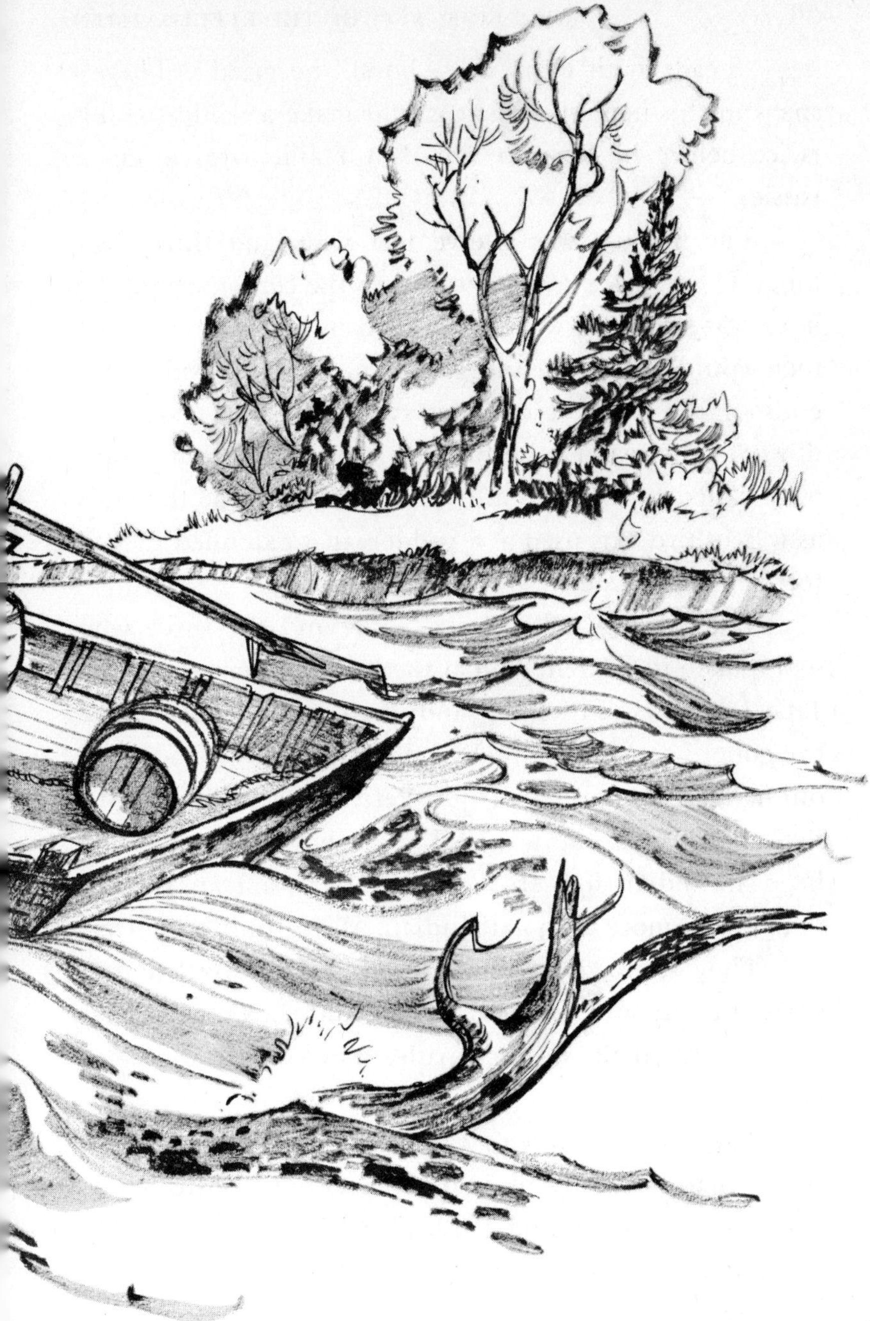

"Steady with them oars, boys!" he cried. "There's snags in this here river that would make a wildcat think twice before he lit into 'em. But I aim to give 'em a tussle!"

The flatboat was twelve feet wide and thirty feet long. There was a covered cabin in the center where the flour was stored. It was surrounded by a low deck so the men could have free movement around the sides and ends of the boat. Two long sweeps or oars extended down to the water, one on each side. These giant oars were called *broadhorns* and were used to guide the craft as was a third oar, used as a rudder, that extended twenty feet beyond the stern.

There was a crew of six. Mike and the three who had spoken in church. And at the last minute, two others. Jabe Knuckles. Thickset, sandy hair and whiskers. One eye gone. Lost in some memorable knock-down-and-drag-out fight. And there was Injun Pete. He was called Injun Pete, not because he was an Indian, but because he had been an Indian fighter. A scout. He wasn't an Indian. Pete wasn't more than half Indian. Maybe only a quarter.

They stopped at night, usually. They pulled into shore, tied up and camped. They could cook on the boat if they wanted to. But as a rule, they cooked and slept on land.

There was plenty to eat. Potatoes and corn meal. And a man could always make a meal out of fish. Someone was usually tending a fish line. They had salt pork, hawg and hominy, and there was plenty of game along the river.

A Scout Becomes a Boatman

As they floated down the Ohio, they learned their lessons. Keep a sharp lookout for snags, always. If they failed, they would lose their cargo and perhaps their lives.

But Mike Fink wasn't really worried. "If I can't keep clear o' the sawyers an' snags an' sand bars, let a yellow-bellied catfish punch a hole in this here boat and take her straight to the bottom!" he said.

Snags were the trees washed into the stream where they stayed to menace the boats. Huge, sharp roots or branches, stabbing out like the unbreakable spines of a giant porcupine. Waiting, ready to stove in the planks of the boat that might run against them.

Planters. These were trees that had been caught by the roots in the river. Their gaunt wind-and-storm-broken limbs lay waiting to pierce through the hull.

Sawyers. Trees caught loosely, that bobbed up and down as the current surged around them.

Sleeping sawyers. The ones that never broke the surface of the water at all. Waiting, secretly, for a victim.

Wooden islands. Great collections of trees. Blown down by storms. Washed loose by floods. Caught, as if by a giant hand, and held by the mud. Huge whirlpools formed back of them, ready to suck a boat under. No telling where one might be. They came and went with the floods. They might even dam up the river and change its course.

Then there was ice, and storms. There were sand bars and islands. Endless dangers.

But it was not all danger. There were happy days.

Quiet nights. Good hunting. Good fishing. Good work. And there were tales. Always tales. They could always open up a bag of talk. There were songs, too.

> Hard upon the beach oar!
> She moves too slow.
> All the way to Shawneetown
> Long time ago.
>
> Some row up, but we row down,
> All the way to Shawneetown.
> Pull away! Pull away!
> Pull away to Shawneetown!

They pulled into Louisville. "Want to hire some men to help you make the portage?" a man asked.

"No," said Mike.

"They ain't no market fer flour here."

"I know," said Mike. "We're goin' through the falls."

"Loaded?"

"Yep. Loaded."

The news spread. Canoes could ride the falls. Small boats had done it. Empty flatboats. But not a fully loaded flatboat. Not a big one.

A crowd collected. "Push off," said Mike.

The boat moved out into the current. Mike moved the rudder. Jabe and Injun Pete worked the broadhorns. "I studied this real keerful," said Mike. "We'll take Injun Chute. The rocks are fifteen feet apart, an' the boat is only twelve feet wide. We kin make her all right if we're cautious. Talbott! You an' Carpenter do what you can with the poles."

The boat picked up speed as the current started to

drop down the Falls of the Ohio. They heard the roar of the rapids. Talbott, Carpenter and Grandpaw Smiley pushed against the rocks and the bottom with their long poles.

Down they went. Water splashed over the gunwales. The bow lurched. It fell. It rose. The stern followed. She wallowed in the waves.

"Hard on the poles!" yelled Mike. "Hold your broadhorn, Jabe! Push her, Pete! Push her hard!"

In a few minutes they dropped twenty-two feet down the rapids. Two miles of nerve-tingling action. Down. Down. Until their boat lurched out of the roughness of the rapids into the smooth, swirling flood of the river.

They heard the noise of a cheer above the grinding roar of the falls. They looked back and saw the people standing on the river bank at Louisville. They were cheering and tossing hats into the air.

Mike and his crew raised their hands and voices in reply. Soon the flatboat left Louisville far behind. But Louisville did not forget. A heavy, fully loaded flatboat had gone down the rapids. The Falls of the Ohio! Mike Fink had done it. Another could do it, too. A hundred more. A thousand. The news spread. The westward march down the Ohio had begun! Mike Fink was on the river!

They went on. Mike was at the helm. Three weeks went by. A thousand miles from home. They were half way.

And then, on an April day, when the sun was shining, they swirled out of the grey-green waters of the Ohio into a brown ocean. Their boat was swung around by a whirlpool. It shuddered and rose and fell in boils of muddy water. They were on the Mississippi!

"Keep 'er steady!" Mike cried. "Man your oars an' give 'em all you've got! Harder on the poles! Push her, Pete! Push 'er hard!"

The Mississippi. They faced bigger snags in this river. At once Mike Fink and his men called her Old Mrs. Sippi. Other people had called her other names. In 1712 the king of France ordered that she be named the River of Saint Louis.

But the king of France was a poor river namer. The Indians who knew the Mississippi had better names. To the Algonquins the river was "Father of the Waters." In the Ojibway tongue it was "River of Water from All Sides." In the Choctaw language it was a combination of two words, "Missah" meaning "Old Big," and "Sippa" meaning "Strong." To the Choctaws, Mississippi meant "Old Big Strong!"

Yes. The Indians knew more about naming rivers. That's what she was. Old Big Strong.

On this great river a flatboat seemed small, a man a weak and helpless thing. But Mike Fink faced her without fear.

When they traveled at night a man stood at the bow listening for the lap of water against a snag, throwing stones out in the dark to test if they were near the shore.

Once, at night, they saw a beautiful white house, gay with lights. They floated past. In an hour, another

A Scout Becomes a Boatman

white house came out of the darkness. Every hour through the night, they passed a beautiful white house. The boatmen wondered that there could be so many white houses all alike.

Then morning came, and in the light of day they discovered they had been in a giant whirlpool all night. They had gone down the stream along the west bank in the current. Then their boat had passed into the eddy and they went back upstream along the east bank, in the eddy. Then downstream in the current, and back again, in the eddy. Again and again. They had been seeing the same white house every hour all night long.

"Look at them snags!" Mike cried. "Them snags is so thick a fish couldn't swim through 'em without rubbin' his scales off an' gettin' blisters on his fins!"

They met and heard and respected something they had never seen before. Alligators.

"Them critters would make a pizen rattlesnake look tame," said Talbott.

They met and talked and fought and sang with the men on other boats, engaged in local and Mississippi river traffic. Creoles. French Canadians. Some Kentuckians. Men from all parts of the world. Tough, hard men, looking for adventure. And finding it.

There was no end of danger, but there was an end of the river. Even the great Mississippi. "There she is! There's New Orleans!" cried Mike. They had made it. On the river all the way.

Mike and Grandpaw Smiley sold their load of flour to eager buyers in New Orleans. They sold the flatboat that had carried them so many miles. Its wood would be used to build houses, barns, factories, warehouses, or even the sidewalks of rapidly growing New Orleans.

Now to go home with gold in their money belts! But how? They could work back on keelboats, but that would take too long. Three or four months to the mouth of the Ohio. That much more on local boats to get home. Going upstream was slow, hard work. They could take a ship to Baltimore or Philadelphia, then overland to their home. Too long, too.

Or they could take the Natchez Trace. That was the way for frontiersmen only lately turned boatmen. The Natchez Trace! Not a road. Not even a trail. But a way, marked by Indians and the tracks of buffalo. No white settlements. No place to buy food. Plenty of snakes and mosquitoes. Too many Indians and bandits.

Mike Fink and his crew set out for Nashville. First to Natchez by boat, then overland to home. They had no horse. They rode shanks mare, and started to walk home.

It was a Sunday evening, six months from the day they left, that Mike and his five companions entered the church at Cross River. There, before startled and joyful eyes, they poured out the gold and silver from New Orleans. The trip from the headwaters of the Ohio to the mouth of the Mississippi was a success. On the rivers. All the way.

"I knowed it could be done," Mike grinned. "That river's as treacherous as runnin' headon into a painter who's had his tail twisted! But it's the river fer me! A fella kin git soft jest stayin' around here scoutin' Injuns."

3. A Trip up Salt River

THE next spring Mike was in Louisville. It was growing rapidly as were all the river towns. There was a bustle and a rush at the river front. He sauntered up to a loaded flatboat. As he drew near he heard an excited conversation.

"Enough men or not enough men," shouted a heavy, florid-faced man to his small, black-bearded companion, "we got to shove off. This high water ain't goin' to last forever."

"But, Henry," said the other, "we got to have enough guns."

"We got ten guns, an' I'm willing to go now. We'll never have enough guns to fight off all the Injuns in Kentucky."

Henry Crist and Solomon Spears were in deep argument. A common argument, too, on the frontier. Indians were always a present danger in Kentucky, and there were never enough guns, it seemed.

Solomon Spears saw Mike Fink standing at the river's edge. The young man was dressed like an Indian scout, but he seemed too young to be in such a skilled and dangerous business. "You bin scoutin'?" he asked.

Mike nodded.

"Any Injun signs around?"

"There's always signs of them varmints," Mike replied.

"See there," Solomon said, turning again to Crist. "We can't risk it."

"If we don't risk it, and right soon, we'll never git this load of salt kettles to Bullitts Lick. They need them kettles for making salt. Anyways, we got a lot of money tied up in them kettles. An' we got a contract."

The contract for salt kettles was important, for salt was one of the most valuable commodities on the frontier. Next to gunpowder and lead. Next to knives and guns. It was necessary to flavor meat and to cure it. The salt licks had been eagerly visited for ages by the wild animals that abounded in Kentucky. Now, the pioneers just as eagerly used the salt springs. They boiled the water away in the huge kettles. The salt remained. At a good salt spring, 120 gallons of water boiled away would leave a gallon of salt in the kettle.

Crist was right. They did have a lot of money invested in the shipment. The kettles had to be delivered and Solomon knew it.

"What you say is right," he said. "The Ohio is at high water. There will be backwater all the way up Salt River, almost clean up to the licks. An' like you say, it ain't goin' to last forever. An' if there ain't no backwater, it will be hard goin' up Salt River with the load we got."

Mike saw his chance to get on the river again. "If you need another gun," he said, "I got one you kin have fer a while, if you're comin' right back."

"We're comin' right back, jest as soon as we unload," said Crist.

Solomon Spears looked at Mike again. He was very young to be an Indian scout. "You look a leetle bit young."

"Young! Why, I was born up the stream a piece so long ago there wasn't a hill big enough to cool off on, or a river big enough to swallow."

"I suppose you kin shoot," Spears said cautiously.

"You suppose I kin shoot?" Mike cried. "Why, I kin outshoot, outfight and outjump any two men west of Pittsburgh — and any three men further east in the land of soft civilization."

The response was so sudden and so determined that Spears backed away nervously.

"What do you think I'm doin' scoutin' fer Injuns if I can't shoot?" Mike shouted. Then he regained control of himself and said in an easy, measured voice, "But I don't mind to limber up my shootin' eye a mite. So if you'll jest do me the favor to sky that tin cup there, I'll prove it!"

Henry Crist's face relaxed into a deep smile. He picked up the cup from the side of the boat. He threw it high in the air. As it sailed up into the sky Mike flashed his rifle to his shoulder. Old Bang All's long barrel described a gentle arc as it followed the rise of the cup. When it reached the peak of its voyage and began slowly to drop, the rifle roared. The cup jerked and flashed in the light like it had been kicked by a thousand sunbeams. It began to spin rapidly, and fell to the ground.

"That ought to make your wings flap," said Mike as he lowered his rifle.

"That's more than good enough fer me," said Crist. "The pay is thirty-seven-and-a-half cents a day. You should have known better, Solomon. He's a young man, but you got to know how to shoot to be an Injun scout."

"You got to know how to shoot to live in this country," Mike said.

"Solomon, you'll learn that after you're here a while longer," said Crist to his partner. Then he turned to Mike. "Come aboard," he said.

Mike and the two men stepped aboard the flatboat. There he saw and met the others. There were thirteen in the party.

"That's thirteen aboard," said Solomon Spears. I hope nobody is superstitious. We got to be keerful. We might have bad luck."

"Everybody's always got to be keerful when there's Injuns around," said Mike. "They're always bad luck."

The flatboat moved into the stream. As Mike stood there watching the land slip away, the feeling for the

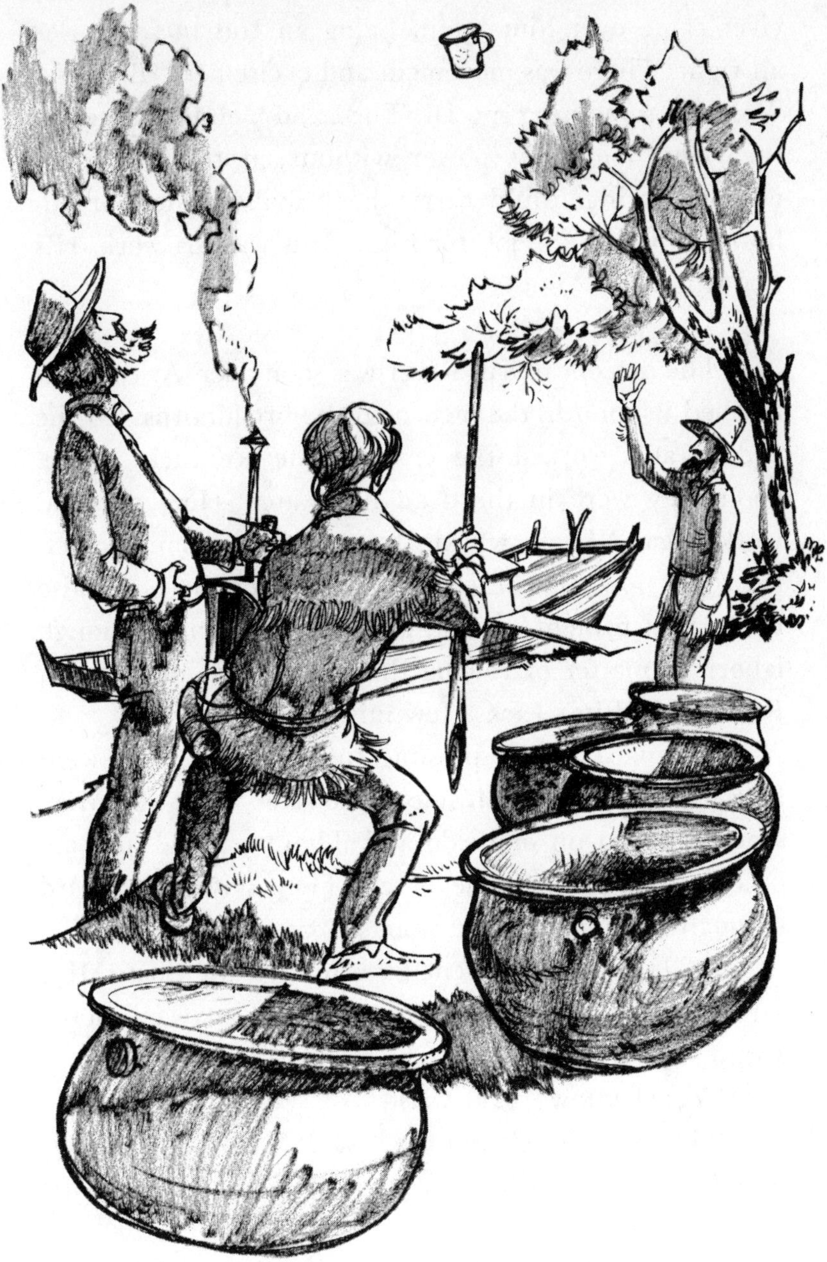

river came over him again. Being an Indian scout was all right. There was movement and excitement. But this! This was something special. The steady, endless surge of the river. Here was power without effort. The river, without trying, could carry the heavily loaded broadhorn. This was the job for him! This was his work. His real work.

The descent to Salt River was soon over. As the boat reached its mouth, the men used the broadhorns and the rudder and worked the craft to the Kentucky shore. Soon they were in the dead backwater. Here the real work began. There was no free, moving current carrying them now. But here in the backwater there was also no current to fight against. Now it was a simple though laborious matter of rowing the big flatboat up the Salt River to Bullitt's Lick a few miles away.

To guard against possible Indian attack, men went forward on land on each side of the river. Crist and Mike scouted ahead on one side and Thomas Floyd and another scout were on the other. They stayed on guard through the night in the woods.

At dawn, as they went back toward the boat, Mike said, "I don't like it. It's too quiet. An' anyway, there's Injun sign around."

"Yes. I know," said Crist.

"There! There's gunfire," said Mike. "It's prob'ly Injuns killin' game fer breakfast. I better go see what they're up to."

"No," said Crist. "Come on. We'll go an' take the

A Trip up Salt River

boat upstream. We'll git out of this Injun neighborhood and have our own breakfast."

"But we ought to know where they are, an' how many of 'em there is. I kin go an' find out," said Mike.

"None of that will make no difference if we ain't around here. I'm sure that shot was off to the southwest."

Mike demurred, but finally assented to his employer's wishes. The flatboat was untied and quietly and quickly worked upstream.

At eight o'clock they tied up to the north bank for breakfast. There was a noise of gobbling turkeys. One of the men named Fossett grabbed his gun and jumped to shore. "Come on," he shouted. "Turkey for breakfast."

"No!" Mike cried. "Wait!" He knew the Indians often made sounds like a turkey to trap the unwary. He wanted to hear it again.

"Wait fer what? I'm hungry," Fossett said as he climbed the bank with Floyd and disappeared into the underbrush.

Mike stood in the bow, rifle ready. He was worried. But perhaps he shouldn't be. Floyd was an old hand at Indian tricks, and he hadn't noticed anything wrong. But somehow, Mike didn't like it. He would have liked to have heard those turkeys gobble again. Just to make sure. He gazed into the deep mass of undergrowth, the tilt of his rifle plainly indicating he was alert.

A volley of gunfire echoed through the forest. The echo was covered by the war whoops of Indians. Fossett and Floyd came running out of the brush. They stumbled and fell down the bank and into the stream.

The flatboat was tied to a tree with a long log chain. It floated free from the land at the chain's end. "Around to the other side!" Mike shouted. The two men obeyed in a rush and a splash.

Mike's rifle cracked. An Indian lunged down the bank. He sprawled out grotesquely and lay quite still at the water's edge.

Mike reloaded. The others on the boat were alert, rifles ready. Fossett and Floyd were helped aboard on the far side where they were protected by the salt kettles from further Indian fire. Fossett had been wounded. He had taken a rifle ball through the fleshy part of his upper arm.

Mike's rifle cracked again. Another hostile folded in the bushes. He tumbled down the bank and lay still beside the first. The little ripples of Salt River lapping at the land began to turn red.

Now the Indians attacked in force. The quiet forest was suddenly filled with war whoops and gunfire. Rifles on the boat rattled deadly reply. Still the enemy came. They swarmed into the river. Their friends, higher on the bank, shot down on the small band in the flatboat.

They were directed by a tall chief. Mike could hear him shout commands. He could almost feel the hate in the screaming directions. He would remember that tall Indian. He would never forget the hate in that voice.

Some of the Indians reached the boat. They tried to pull it into shore. They were met with rifle butts and knives. Mike was in the thick of it, in the midst of hand-to-hand fighting. The injured on the boat loaded the

A Trip up Salt River

guns, but there was little time to shoot now. When there was no loaded rifle, a knife was good enough to cut through those trying to climb on the boat.

The Indians at length withdrew to the safety of the upper bank. There, protected by the trees, they continued to fire down on the flatboat. The boat was in a desperate position. It must be moved.

But it could not move. The heavy log chain fastened it securely to the tree. The chain was wrapped around the tree trunk and fastened with its hook in a link. There was no way to release the hook.

"That chain has got to be unfastened," said Mike.

"But how? This end is bolted on the boat," said Crist.

"Then it's got to be undone at the tree," said Mike.

He stripped off his heavy buckskin jacket, and slid into the water on the flatboat's far side. The dark water of Salt River was quiet. Clusters of bubbles floated easily on the surface. There was no sound, except the crack of rifles and the thud and splash when a bullet hit the water. Or a thud and a flare of splinters when the broadhorn's heavy wood was struck.

Crist was watching the chain through a crack between the wall of kettles on the shore side. Suddenly Mike arose out of the water at the foot of the tree. He seized the chain and released the hook. The heavy chain, pulled by its own weight, slid around the muddy roots and down into the water, like a heavy black snake.

The hostiles turned their fire on Mike. His eyes turned upward and there above him he saw the tall chief's evil face, a mask of rage and hate. He saw the Indian's arm slash through the air. He saw a tomahawk flash.

Mike lifted his arm. His gesture saved his life, for his hand caught the hatchet's force and turned it away from his throat.

Mike sank out of sight in the dark protection of the flood water. Blood from his injured hand stained the river water and faded away.

Drops of hot lead from the bank hit the water and made angry little geysers. A long moment passed. Too long. Had one of the venomous missiles found its mark? No. Mike's head broke water on the far side of the boat. In another moment he was aboard. The chain was drawn up and the flatboat moved to the other shore and safety.

4. On the River

THE flatboat made its way back to Louisville after delivering the kettles at the Salt Licks, and Mike made his way back to Pittsburgh. His hand had healed. The raw scar left by the tomahawk was fading. But the scar within him remained. On the frontier, Indians were enemies. They always had been. But now Mike Fink carried a burden of enmity that would not erase. The scene flashed through his mind again and again. The flying tomahawk, the sharp pain, the upraised, bleeding hand. One day, he knew it, one day he would meet that tall Indian with the evil face!

But now Mike's mind was made up. He was going on the river once and for all. And for good. Not as a casual laborer. Not as an extra hand on a flatboat. He was going to get a regular job on a keelboat.

Almost every young man along the river wanted to "push a keel." The blast of the boatmen's horns, the sound of their songs made the adventurous yearn to drop their plows and axes and take up a keelboatman's pole.

River traffic was growing fast. Keelboats, of shallow draft, and far more maneuverable than the flatboats, were the latest thing. A far cry from the bullboats once in common use on the western waters. Bullboats, covered with buffalo hides, with a stick and the shoulder blade of the animal for oars. A far cry from barges and flatboats, too, for the keelboat could go up fast-moving streams, and to the far reaches of small rivers.

Jobs on keelboats were hard to get. A man had to prove himself.

Baptiste was a Creole who had spent his life on the Mississippi. With the development of the upper Ohio Valley he had extended his operations. His keelboat was tied up in Pittsburgh. Mike went down to the river to see it.

Baptiste's keelboat was forty feet long and had a nine-foot beam. It was a trim craft and well built. Unlike a flatboat, it was shaped at both ends. She drew no more than two feet of water. There was a cargo box or cabin in the center. A cleated footway eighteen inches wide ran around the boat between the gunwales and the cabin. In the bow there were seats for eight oarsmen. The helmsman stood on a platform at the stern and steered with a long oar that was pivoted on the boat. She could

On the River

carry thirty or forty tons of freight.

Mike walked up to a boatman. "When you goin' to leave?" he asked.

The man grinned. "Soon. In an hour," he said.

"Who's the captain?"

"Ah. Zee patroon, eh? He ees Baptiste," was the reply.

"Where is he? I mean, where's Baptiste?" Mike asked.

A heavy, grimy thumb jabbed in the direction of the patroon.

"You Baptiste?"

"Oui."

"I want a job."

"Ah, no. Sorree. No place."

"I'm Mike Fink."

"Ah, yes. You shoot ze rifle I have heard. Good. You have ze keen eye. Like ze panthaire. But I need more zan zat."

"What?"

"I need ze fightaire. I need ze muscles."

"I got muscles. I kin fight."

A Creole shrug was the answer.

"I'm the original Salt River roarer. I'm spilin' fer a fight right now. I'm as ready as a race horse with a light rider. I can outswim, outtalk, outjump, outfight any man this side of Catfish Bend. I'm painfully ferocious. I'm spilin' fer someone to whip me. If you got a creetur in this diggin' that wants to be disappointed in trying to do it, let him yell!"

The Creole thumb jerked toward a black-bearded giant standing near Mike. There was another Creole shrug and a fine Creole smile. The big man looked down at Mike with a broad, easy Kentucky grin.

"He's my man," cried Mike. "And that one, too!"

Mike was really talking big now, for he included a second burly keelboatman in his invitation to fight. "I'm as eager as a cat at a mouse picnic!"

With no more preliminaries there was a flurry of arms and legs as the three mixed head on. Mike feinted and dodged, slipped and ducked, and gave two blows for one.

A crowd gathered. The end came soon. Mike stepped aside to avoid a giant's lunge. His foot shot out. The giant tripped and fell. The other big man took an honest punch on the nose and another at the belt line. He buckled like a belt and joined his fallen comrade on the ground.

Mike turned to Baptiste. "You are ze man, not only of iron, but also of heeckory and of buckskeen! You got ze job," the Creole patroon said.

Baptiste took out a thumbworn black book and a pencil. "I weel put your name in ze book. How you spell heem?"

"They tell me the best keelboaters is Creoles and French Canadians," Mike said.

"Ah, oui," Baptiste answered. "But ze Kantucks, zey are strong. Zey are ze fightaires. Zey are good, too."

"Well, anyway, my name is Mike Fink. You spell it down in your book like this: M-i-c-h-e P-h-i-n-c-k. That'll

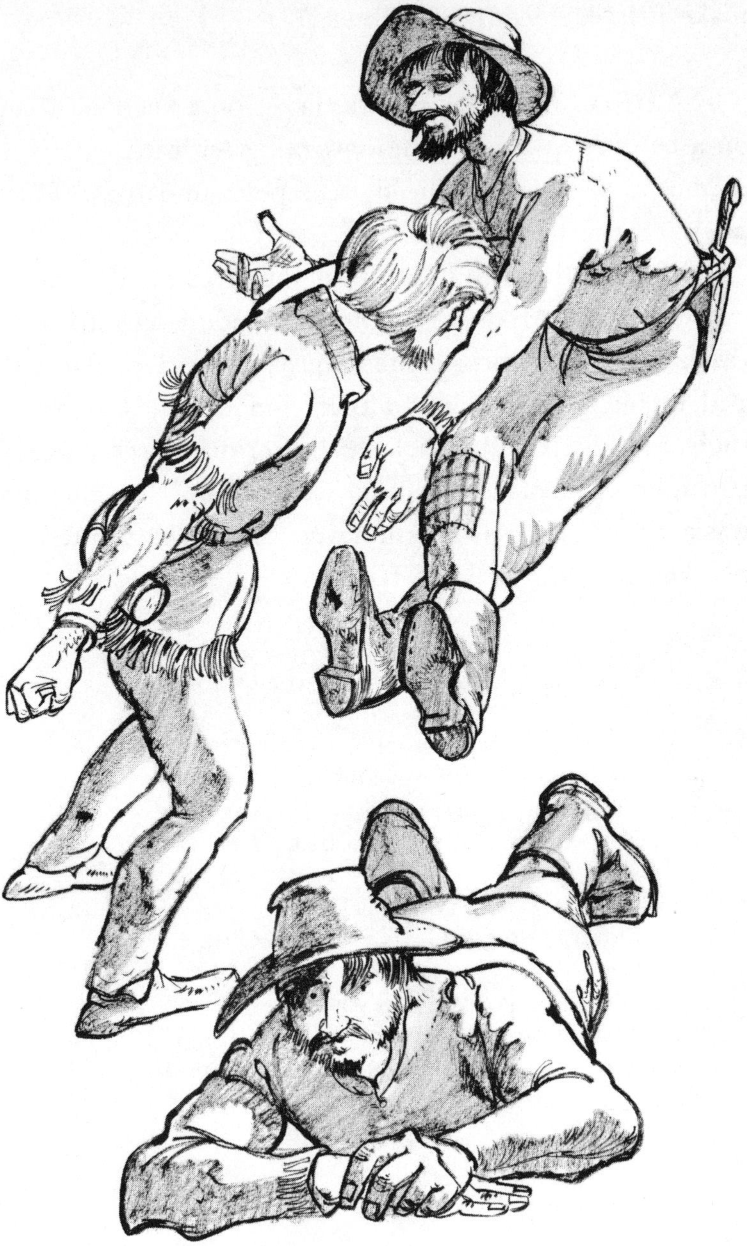

make it look a leetle bit French."

A trip to New Orleans was faster on a keelboat than on a flatboat. Mike was now working with skilled river men who were experienced with poles and oars. They knew all the tricks.

The keelboat put out into the stream. The boatmen sang, and Mike Fink sang the loudest. He stood in the bow with his face to the length of the river. He was still in buckskin. He stood there among the keelers in their red shirts, blue jackets, butternut linsey-woolsey pants, heavy boots and tanned leather caps. But now he was a keeler. He was on the river. Where he wanted to be. And he sang with the rest:

> Hi-O, away we go,
> Floating down the river on the Ohio.
>
> When the boatman goes ashore
> He spends his money and works for more.
> I never saw a girl in all my life,
> But what she would be a boatman's wife.
>
> Hi-O, away we go,
> Floating down the river on the Ohio.
>
> The boatman is a lucky man;
> No one can do as the boatman can.
> The boatmen dance, and the boatmen sing,
> The boatman is up to everything.
>
> Hi-O, away we go,
> Floating down the river on the O-hi-O.

On the way down the river Mike met the other keel-

On the River

boatmen. He learned the trade, sang the songs and fought the fights. He saw the sights and the colors of Limestone, Louisville, New Memphis, Natchez-Under-the-Hill, New Orleans and the other river towns.

When he got to New Orleans he thought he was a real keelboater. When he got back, he knew he was. The trip upstream — "fernenst" stream, they called it — separated the men from the boys. It separated the keelboatmen from farmers. It separated the real men from all other men.

The patroon hired returning flatboatmen to supplement the crew to go fernenst stream. There was no helpful current going fernenst stream. The current now was against them. An opponent. To be overcome in any way possible. With the river, it was no fair fight. It was rough and tumble. The keelboatmen made an inch, a yard, or a mile any way they could.

First, there were the poles. Twenty feet long. With an iron point on one end and a heavy knob on the other. The poles were used when the river bottom was firm and the water shallow enough for them to reach the bottom. At Baptiste's shouted command, "Stand to your poles!", the men would take up their poles and go forward. At the command, "Toss poles!", the spiked ends were placed in the water. Then, standing along the sides, half the men on each side, they would set the spiked ends on the bottom at the command, "Set poles!".

At the patroon's shout, "Down on her!", they would put the knob against their shoulder and push with all their might. As the combined push overcame the current, the boat would move slowly upstream. They would have pushed their load a few feet of the 2,000 miles between New Orleans and Pittsburgh.

As the polemen pushed down, they moved along the cleated runway to the stern. When the first man reached the stern, the command was "Lift poles!". Then they would straighten up and, dragging their poles in the water, walk forward to repeat the operation and push the boat ahead a few more feet.

Mike worked with the rest. He pushed his pole and he sweated with the rest. His hands were calloused and his muscles bulged like the knots and knurls on a hickory log. Getting a keelboat upstream took real men. But Mike Fink was a real man.

When the river bottom fell away and the poles could not be used, oars were worked to go upstream.

In deep water and fast current, where neither poles nor oars could be used to push the boat fernenst stream, there was the cordelle. The cordelle was a tow line, several hundred feet, even a thousand feet long. One end was hitched to the mast. The boatmen would swim to shore, one with the other end of the tow line in his teeth. On the river bank they cleared away the brush and trees so they would have a place to walk as they pulled on the cordelle. They carried guns to protect themselves in case of Indian attacks. Old Bang All came in handy. And they carried the cordelle and slowly pulled the heavy weight of the keelboat upstream.

The slowest method of all in trying to move a boat fernenst stream was known as "warping." Taking the

On the River

cordelle ahead in a skiff, one of the boatmen would fasten it to a snag, a planter, a tree, or a rock by a pulley and run the end back to the keelboat. Then the men on the boat would take up the rope with a capstan or a windlass and pull the boat forward. In a long day of warping, to make six miles was considered very good.

There was another way, too. Bushwhacking. If the river was high, the men grabbed hold of the bushes and tree branches along the shore and used them to pull the boat forward. And when the wind was right, they put up a sail. Anything to move the craft against the current.

Always there were snags, planters and sawyers to guard against. Mike took his turn watching for them.

Sometimes they crossed the river to take advantage of better conditions on the other side. But at each crossing, the current would carry the boat back downstream, perhaps as much as half a mile or more. Sometimes they made as many as 390 crossings between New Orleans and St. Louis. On a long trip fernenst stream, as from New Orleans to Pittsburgh, a boat in crossing might slip backwards as many as 500 hard-won miles.

Going fernenst stream was all work! Every inch of the way. A keelboat did well to average fifteen miles a day. A man pulled or pushed or rowed, and it was callous-making, blister-breeding, muscle-maiming, bone-bruising work. But Mike Fink was on the river, and he was glad. Here was real excitement. Here was a real test of strength and courage. He would have his own keelboat some day!

When the river was at flood stage, they went downstream fast. But fernenst stream, it was slow and hard. Old Mrs. Sippi could rise sixty feet. At the rate of ten feet an hour. She could sink as fast. The Ohio could do almost as much. When a flood came, the mooring cables could snap like threads. Or, if they didn't break, the rope could hold the boat down while the rising waters flooded in and sank her. When a flood passed, the boat might be left on a sand bar, or in sloppy mud, away from the stream. When this happened, the boatmen got the craft back in the current any way they could. They used the cordelle. They used horses, if horses could be found. They even dug canals to float their boat once again to the river.

The men who handled the keelboats worked hard. They fought hard. They played hard. They talked hard. They boasted hard. They *were* hard! And the hardest of them all was Mike Fink. A man of hickory and rawhide as well as of iron.

The boatmen, with their bare hands and against the strength of the river, moved the people of a growing nation and their freight.

Fernenst stream on a keelboat it was pole and warp, tow and row, and row and tow, and warp and pole! And whether poling or warping or towing or rowing, they kept time and worked together with a song:

> Dance, boatman, dance.
> Dance, dance away.
> Dance all night till broad daylight,
> And go home with the gals in the morning.

5. Screamers, Roarers and the Red Feather

MIKE went back and forth between Pittsburgh and New Orleans. To St. Louis. A half-dozen times or more. On Baptiste's keelboat. On another keelboat. On flatboats and barges. He was a riverman! Sometimes Talbott or the boy, Carpenter, or Jabe Knuckles or Injun Pete shipped with him. Sometimes they went on different boats. But they met on the river or in the river towns. They tried to travel together, but it was not always possible. A man had to take a job where he could find one.

Rivermen were a rough and rugged crew. Veterans of a lifetime of Indian fighting, of a dozen Indian wars.

They wore shirts of bright red wool or fringed buckskin, or no shirt at all when they were working. Pants of linsey-woolsey, butternut stained, or of buckskin. Coats of blanket cloth or buckskin. Heavy leather boots or moccasins. A fur or leather cap. A wide leather belt which held a dirk, or a bowie knife. Arkansas toothpicks, they called the knives. They usually carried a rifle or a pistol.

They ate hawg and hominy, game, potatoes, hardtack, corn meal boiled with tallow. They drank the river water and boasted that "the sand in the water scours out the innards, and the more one drinks of it, the healthier he gets."

Someone of the crew usually could scrape a tune out of a fiddle. They called the fiddler "pappy" and the fiddle, "katy." Where they could, they pushed or rowed or pulled in time to music.

When a crewman moved from one boat to another he carried his possessions tied up in a bandana. His plunder, he called it. As they came and went they met at night or on Sunday on the river banks in a hundred places. Natchez-Under-the-Hill. Shawneetown. Louisville. New Madrid. St. Louis. Grand Tower of the Mississippi. The Devil's Bake Oven.

They initiated the first trippers by shaving their heads or ducking them in the river. They wrestled and fought, and sang and danced, and talked and bragged and yarned. There was among them a real comradeship, based on their devotion to their job. They were "thicker than black bugs in spiled ham."

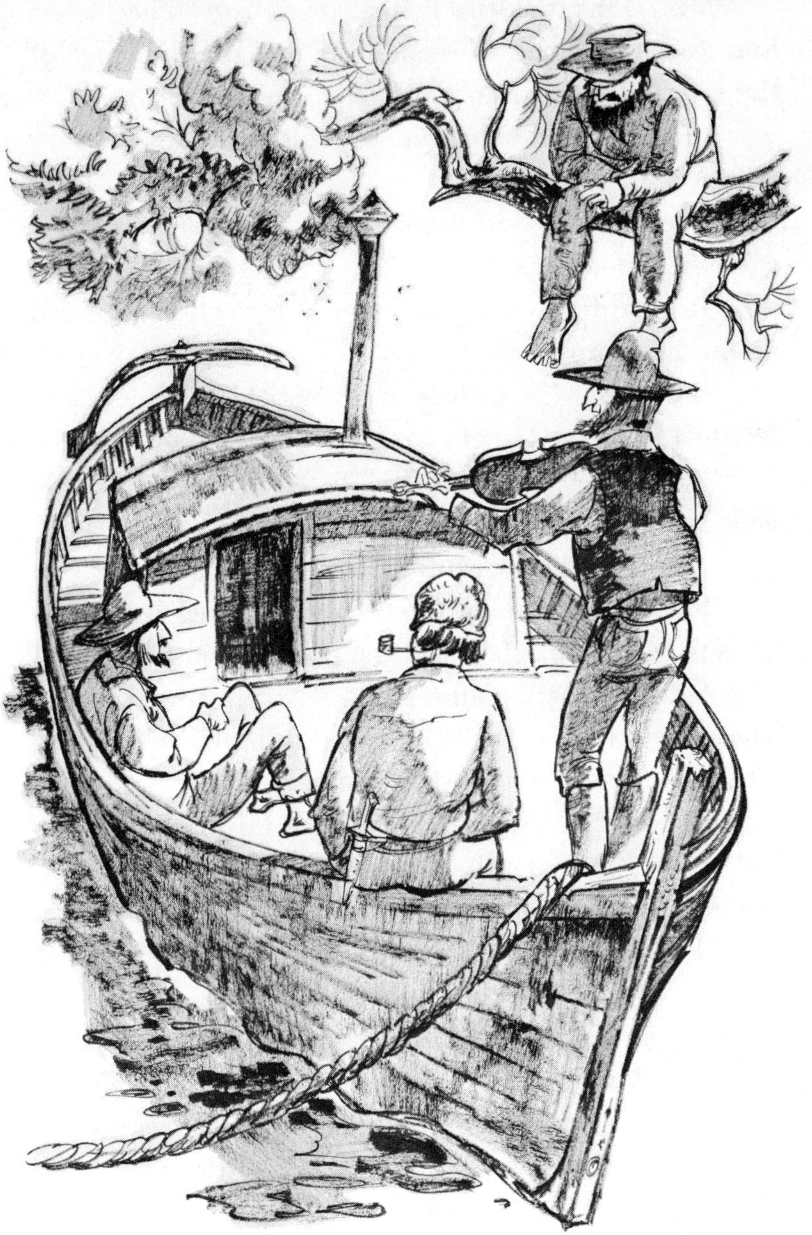

Mike Fink was the first among them. They knew him well, these men who endlessly met the challenge of the river with endurance, muscle, courage and skill.

"That mannee is slicker'n greased lightnin'," they said.

"He's always skitin' about like a weasel in a barnyard."

"It's harder to whip him than it is to climb a peeled saplin' heels upards."

"I'd jest as leave chase a bar in a holler tree trunk feet first as to try to fight him."

"When you see him, you better throw your pole wide an' brace off."

"He's heap brave with plenty of grit."

The best fighter on the river wore a red feather in his cap. Mike Fink soon had the feather, and he kept it! The fights he had! Fair fights, or rough and tumble, where there were no rules and everything was fair. They could take their choice. Mike didn't care!

He was the best of the boatmen. His challenge was wide open: "I'm a Salt River roarer! I'm a ring-tailed screamer! I'm a Massassip squealer! I'm chock-full o' fight! I'm half wild horse and half cockeyed alligator, an' the rest of me is crooked snags an' red hot snappin' turkle. I can hit like fourth proof lightnin', an' every lick I make lets in an acre of sunshine. I can outrun, outjump, outshout, outbrag and outfight, rough and tumble, no holts barred, any man on both sides of the river from Pittsburgh to New Orleans an' back again to St. Louie. Come, all you flatters, you bargers, you milk-white me-

Screamers, Roarers and the Red Feather

chanics, an' see how tough I am to chaw. I ain't had a fight fer a whole day, an' I'm spilin' fer exercise!"

There was plenty to do. Running. Jumping. Shouting. Bragging. Fighting. Mike was the best.

Fighting! A test of strength. It was all good fun. And the contestants were firm friends after the test was over.

There was Billy Earthquake. What a man! Six feet four! All man. Shoulders like a bear's. Arms and legs like the four quarters of a bull buffalo. Strong! A face like last year's bird's nest. When he saw Mike Fink with the red feather in his cap, Billy Earthquake said, "This is me an' no mistake! Billy Earthquake! I kin whip any man anywhere!"

He pointed a long, thick finger at Mike. "An' that includes you! Come an' try to fight me! Maybe you don't know me. I towed a broadhorn up Salt River where the snags were so thick the fish couldn't swim without rubbing their scales off!"

"I'm achin' to fight you," Mike replied. "I'm a screamer myself. I'll walk tall into you!"

Billy Earthquake went on, "Why, once a horse kicked me an' put both his hips out of joint. With one squint I kin blister a bull's heel. I'm tough! I'll live forever an' then turn into a white oak post!"

Mike lunged at him, quicker than action. A crowd gathered and cheered. They fought, and Mike Fink whipped him, rough and tumble. Billy for a while looked like a white oak post. Stiff and motionless.

Then, there was Skippoweth Branch. A bundle of

muscle! When he saw Mike Fink with the red feather, there was covetousness in his heart muscle. "I'm the bully of Salt River," he roared. "I sleep in my hat an' chaw my vittles with my front teeth! An' I scream through my nose! I sun myself in thunderstorms and ride to meeting on two horses an' never turn out fer man nor beast. I have sworn to lick everything I see, except my father and my mother. An' I see you!"

He glowered at Mike who returned his gaze. Such a friendly, cordial invitation to see who was the best man could not be ignored, so Mike answered, "An' I see you, an' I'm glad to say I'm no relation. I'd walk ten miles any day or night to fight you!"

Skippoweth had more to say. He was as proud of his challenge as he was of fighting. "I'm a great oak that grows half my length underground and turns my roots up unexpected. My name is floating iron and melted pewter. You can call me red hot cannon balls or the Big Snag of the desert."

Mike outshouted him. "An' I'm Mike Fink. The Snapping Turkle of the Ohio! The Snag of the Massassip! I'm ready for you!"

But Skippoweth was not finished. He wouldn't hold back a wrestling hold or a punch. Nor would he hold back a word or a phrase. It gave the crowd time to gather. It gave the contestants time to get the measure of the other. "I live in the mountains and I eat thunder! I wear a neck cloth made of chain lightnin'. An' I will never come to my full height till the clouds are lifted a piece. Call me a west wind full of prickles. Or a dose of old

Screamers, Roarers and the Red Feather

Kentuck. Or a hunk of the Allegheny Mountains. I kin outscream seven catamounts!"

Perhaps so. But he couldn't outfight Mike Fink. Mike was at him. Slick and smooth as a wildcat. And Mike Fink whipped him, rough and tumble.

There was Jim Girty, nephew of an infamous renegade. Mike first met him at Natchez-Under-the-Hill. Jim was a veteran of river fights and coveted the red feather that flashed jauntily on Mike's cap.

"There's Jim Girty," said Talbott.

"He ain't no screamer," Jabe Knuckles said. "Guns an' knives don't make no diff'rence to Jim Girty. No kind of fighting' makes no diff'rence to Jim Girty. He ain't got no ribs."

"No ribs?"

"That's right. No ribs! They say his chest is jest plain boiler-plate. No ribs."

"Stay away from him, Mike. He's dynamite and iron," Jabe added.

"If he wants to try fer the red feather, I'll meet him. Anyway, I ain't had a real good fight fer a week. If I don't have one soon, I'll spile. Like a four-day-old catfish on a sand bar."

There on the river front at Natchez-Under-the-Hill, that's where they met. That's where Jim Girty claimed the red feather in Mike's hat. That's where the two big boatmen clashed. Like two bolts of lightning crashing together in a hickory forest.

On the river front at Natchez-Under-the-Hill. The crowd was cheering and whooping. That's where Mike

Fink got his arm around big Jim Girty's chest. That's where the muscles in Mike Fink's arms knotted like black oak burls, and tightened like wet buckskin.

Jim Girty's chest resisted. The keelers and the flatters and the bargers stopped their whoops and shouts. The screamers stopped screaming. There was a long pause.

It was not true. Jim Girty did not have a solid, cast-iron chest. He gave up. He said, "Enough."

And Mike Fink still had the red feather!

There was Jack Pierce. Famed as a man with a real hard head. He once won a butting contest with a maddened ram. His attack in the river fights was head first.

When Jack Pierce met Mike Fink he stamped his feet and shouted, "I'm a land screamer! I can lick nine times my own weight in wildcats! I want that red feather! I'll jump down your throat quicker than a streak of lightnin' can go down a swamp cypress!"

Mike grinned and ran his fingers over the feather, his crown of victory of a hundred fights.

The fight was on! Jack Pierce lowered his head and rushed toward Mike. Mike lowered his own skull and charged. The two heads met. Mike Fink kept the red feather!

The screamers on the river shouted their fighting challenges, like the bull alligator in the swamp, like the bull buffalo on the prairie, like the rooster in the barnyard. An open invitation to the world. They would test their strength and courage and skill with all comers.

There was Roaring Ralph Stackpole. "Whar's your

6. The "Lightfoot"

MIKE hired out as a captain. Once they gave him a flatboat made of rotton wood. Kentucky boats, they called them. The wood gave away, and she sank. The owner, Mr. Winchester sued Mike, alleging he was negligent and that the boat sank because of his negligence.

"Negligent? That sounds like neglect," Mike shouted. "No such thing! The wood was rotten. It wouldn't hold against a snag. Why, it was so rotten I could push holes in it with my little finger!"

The suit was tried before Dr. Justice Richardson in Pittsburgh. Mike intended to prove his point. He went to the wreck of the old rotting boat they had given him to command. He dove down and tore loose a couple of

Screamers, Roarers and the Red Feather

buffalo bull," he cried, "that kin cross ho[rns with a] roarer from Salt River? Whar's your full-[blooded horse] than kin shake a saddle off? Whar's your [ ] rolling prairies? H'yars the old brown bar th[at can rip] the bark off a gum tree. H'yar's a man fer yo[u!] An' you! Aren't I a ring-tailed squealer? I c[an tote the] Salt River on my back, an' swim up the O[hio. Whar's] the man to fight Roaring Ralph Stackpole?"

Mike Fink was the man! Fight him, he d[id, and] kept the red feather.

The years sped on. Mike Fink went up [and down] the river. Work. Hunt. Sing. Dance. Fight. Al[ways fight.] There was Mike Wolf. There was Billy Sed[ley whose] "heart was as big as an apple barrel." Tom Bru[ce.] Big Nose. Sim Roberts. The fights were a part [of life] and each opponent became a firm friend. Read[y to fight] again, perhaps, but a friend.

the rotten planks and took them to court. Anybody could see by looking at them that the boat had not been kept in good repair.

The Justice delivered his opinion: "This court had the misfortune once to place valuable cargo on a Kentucky boat, not knowing it to be such; which sunk and went down in seventeen feet of water, this court believed by coming in contact with a yellow-bellied catfish, there being no snag or rock or other obstruction near her at the time. And this court being satisfied with the premises in this case doth order that the same be dismissed at the plaintiff's cost, to have included therein the expenses of the defendant's costs, in going to and returning from the wreck, for the purpose of obtaining such damnable and irrefutable evidence as this bottom plank has furnished."

"The judge was right," Mike said. "That wood was so rotten it would of busted if a catfish had nudged against it."

"Sure," said Carpenter, "an' that's probably what happened, too. It certainly wasn't your fault, Mike."

"Right," Talbott agreed. "It was jest the wood. It was rotten."

Mike made his own keelboat and became a patroon. His own captain. That's what a man did who wanted a boat. Designed it himself and built it himself.

He named her the *Lightfoot*. Fast and rugged, like her owner. She drew less water than any other keelboat and Mike could take her up the swiftest rapids and in the shallowest waters, as well as the deepest. He could

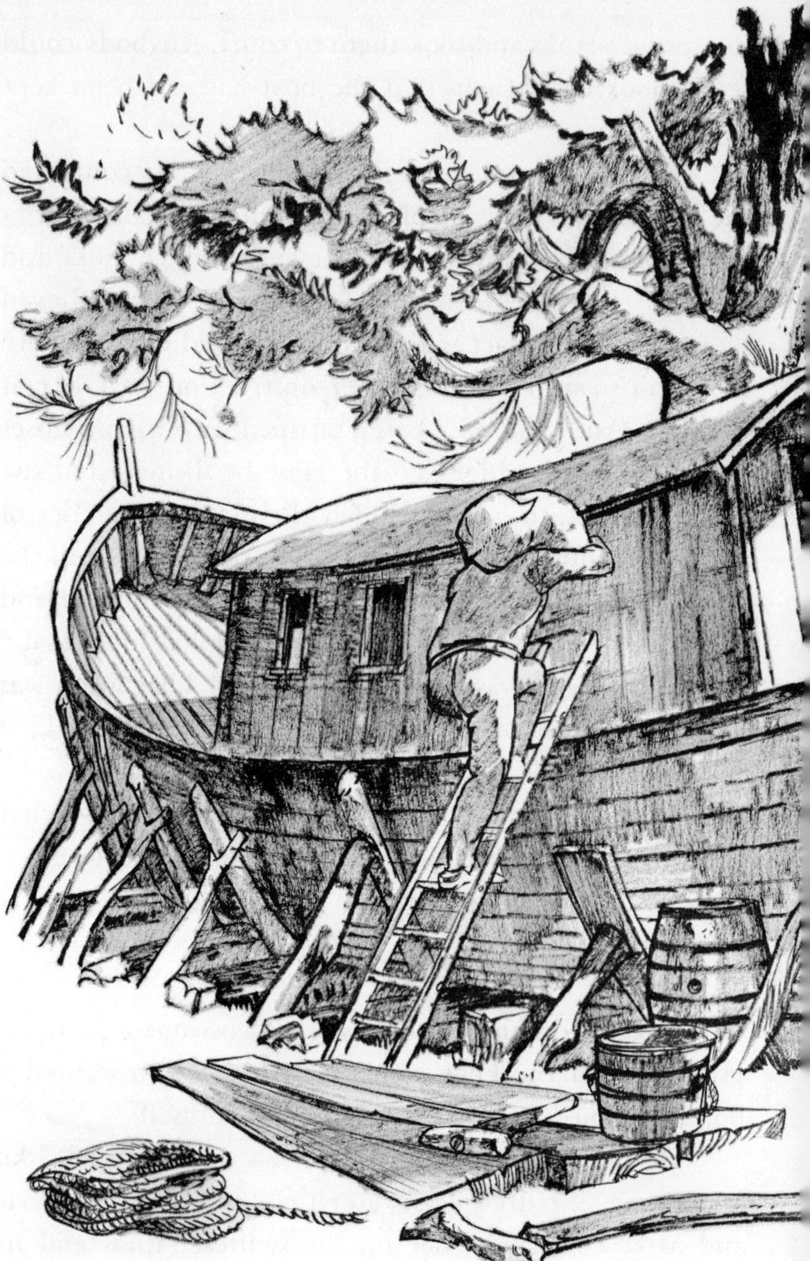

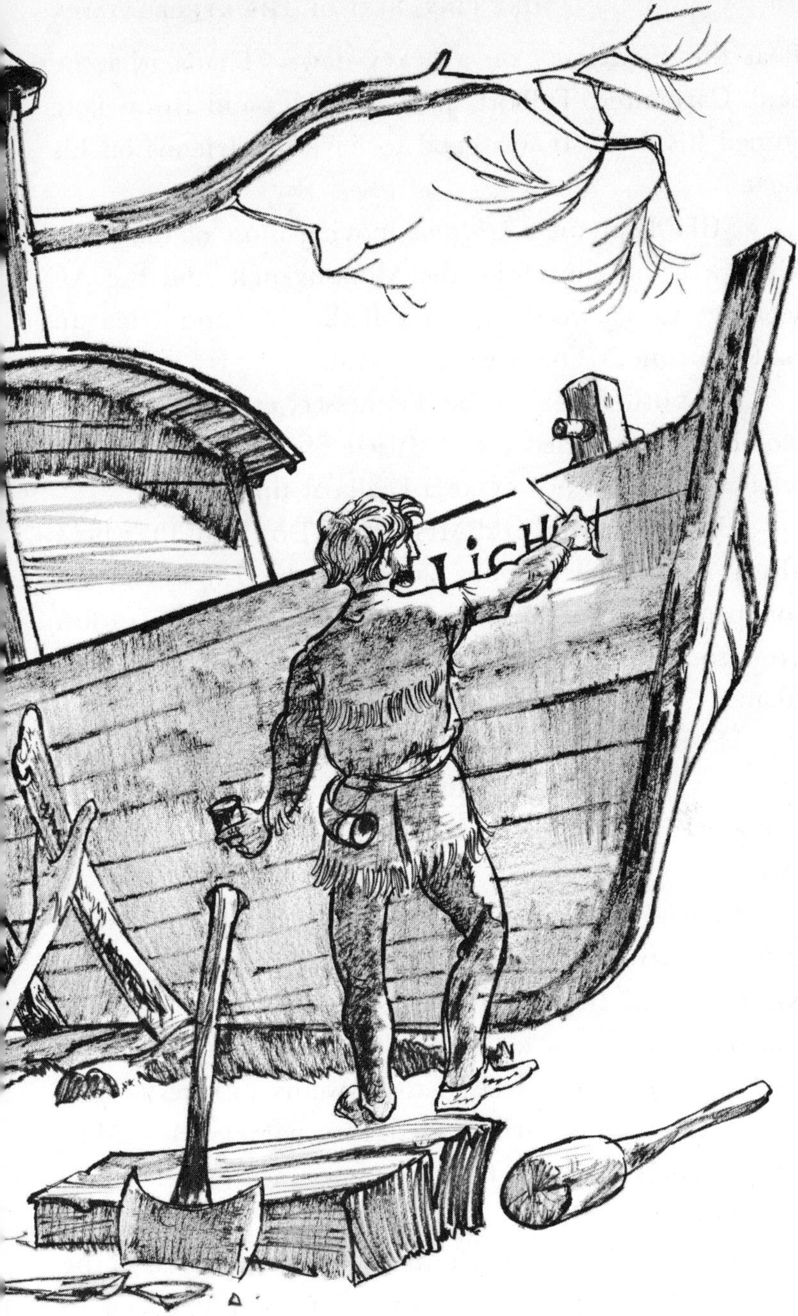
LicH

float the *Lightfoot* "on a heavy dew." That's what he said. Carpenter, Talbott, Jabe Knuckles and Injun Pete joined his crew. It was good to have old friends on his boat.

Mike kept the *Lightfoot* moving most of the time. Up north, on the Ohio, the Monongahela and the Allegheny, which were "frozen half the time and dried up half the time." That's what he said.

He pushed her on the Tennessee, even above Muscle Shoals. He called them Muscle Shoals because that's what it took lots of to take a keelboat up them.

He took her on Old Mrs. Sippi. Down south, where alligators scratched their backs on the *Lightfoot* and snapped the poles in two. Up north, where the catfish grew so thick it was hard to push a keelboat through them.

He pushed her on the Missouri, and the Red, and on half a hundred other apron strings of Old Mrs. Sippi. Ribbons of water that fed and bound and held half a continent.

Up and down the rivers he went. Fighting the snags and the current with Talbott and Carpenter and Jabe Knuckles and Injun Pete. These good men, these firm friends were always with him. Ten men could take the *Lightfoot* down the river. It took twenty to take her upstream. He hired returning flatters or bargers who didn't want to walk back on the Natchez Trace or return by boat to Philadelphia.

A fast keelboat, well built and well managed, as the *Lightfoot* was, could go downstream at the rate of one to

The "Lightfoot"

five miles an hour, depending on the stage of the river. She could go from Pittsburgh to New Orleans in four to six weeks. The return trip took three to four months.

Mike built another keelboat, and hired a patroon for her. He laid his boats up at his home near Wheeling. His friends, Daniel Boone and Davy Crockett, came to visit him when he was home, and sometimes he met them on the river.

Everyone on the river knew him. Everyone else had heard of him. The Snag of the Mississippi! The Snapping Turtle of the Ohio!

Mike Fink had a wife and a daughter. Their names were Sal. Often they went with him on the *Lightfoot*. They knew the river and the ways of frontier life almost as well as Mike knew them.

Sal Fink, the daughter, was courted for a time by Davy Crockett's son, Hardstone Crockett. She was real purty, Hardstone thought. So did Mike. A sweet girl. Sweet enough, almost, to pour on corn cakes.

Sal Fink, the daughter, was the image of Sal Fink, the mother. A description of one is almost certainly a description of the other. Sal Fink, the mother, had a bear for a lap dog. She was different, Sal was. She compared to other women as an old she-bear to a little kitten. A woman worthy of the mighty Mike Fink.

Sal Fink, the daughter, was a girl who once killed a bear with her fists. She was thus described by an honest man who knew and loved her well:

"She fought a duel once with a thunderbolt an'

came off without a single scratch, while at fust fire, she split the thunderbolt all to flinders, an' gave the pieces to Uncle Sam's artillerymen to touch off their cannon with. When a gal about six years old, she used to play see-saw on the Mississippi snags, and arter she war done she would snap 'em off, an' so cleared a large district of the river. She used to ride down the river on an alligator's back, standen upright, an' dancing *Yankee Doodle,* and could leave all the steamers behind."

Yes. Sal Fink was quite a girl.

Mrs. Crockett often came with her husband, Colonel David Crockett, to visit on the river above Wheeling where the Finks lived. One night, in the spirit of good fun, Mike tried to scare her. He hid inside an alligator skin. He howled so loud he scared himself, but he didn't frighten Mrs. Crockett.

He crawled close and grabbed her. She threw him a flash of eye lightning that made it seem like daylight for an hour. Then she drew her Arkansas toothpick. She swung at the alligator, and the knife cut off the alligator head and shaved the top hair off Mike's head. Then Mrs. Crockett went after the alligator with her fists and gave Mike the only real punishment he had ever had. Mrs. Crockett didn't realize it was Mike and that he was only joking until it was too late. And, of course, Mike was a gentleman and didn't fight back.

After that, he entertained Mrs. Crockett like a Colonel's lady, and didn't try to frighten her again.

But for Mike there was more than the fun of fighting river screamers. There was more than the fun and

The "Lightfoot" 73

danger of trying to frighten Mrs. Crockett. There was more to life than raising a daughter.

He pulled his keelboat off a dozen sand bars. He broke acres of river ice to keep his boat afloat. Once he killed a moose with no weapon other than an Arkansas toothpick with a broken blade. He beat a bear to death with his bare hands, and he drowned a wolf that had attacked him from the rear while he was fishing. Once, when his craft was stove in by a rock and seemed sure to sink, he threw a buffalo robe overboard so the suction of the water drew it into the hole and stopped the leak.

Mike shot tin cans from the top of Carpenter's head. A foolish and dangerous trick, even for the best shot on the river. He never missed.

With Bang All in his hands, and the *Lightfoot* beneath his feet, Mike Fink was one to be reckoned with. The work of building the west went on, and the Salt River Roarer, the Snappin' Turtle of the Ohio, the Snag of the Massassip was in its midst.

The river carried every kind of craft man could devise. Men were thinking and working and trying to make something better all the time.

The river saw boats with paddle wheels operated by men, and by horses. Then the paddles were powered by steam engines. The engines were always breaking down. Repairs were hard to make. Parts were hard to get. Fuel was hard to get. They couldn't go in low water. Almost everyone was sure they would never replace keelboats and men with poles.

Mike Fink sneered at the steamers and said, "I'd

like to see them new-fangled merchines try to go up Horse Tail Ripple or Letart's Falls. Get up them without the aid of good setting poles or cordelles. It couldn't be done no how."

Zadok Cramer published a book telling how to navigate the rivers. Soon he published a new edition every year. It was in great demand. It was called *The Navigator: Containing Directions for Navigating the Monongahela, Alleghany, Ohio and Mississippi Rivers; With an Ample Account of these Much Admired Waters, from the Head of the Former to the Mouth of the Latter; and a Concise Description of their Towns, Villages, Harbours, Settlements, Etc. With Accurate Maps of the Ohio and Mississippi: To Which is Added an Appendix Containing an Account of Louisiana, and of the Missouri and Columbia Rivers as Discovered by the Voyage under Captains Lewis and Clark. 6th Ed. Pitts. 1808.*

The *Lightfoot* was only one of the many craft on the rivers. One hundred boats landed in a single day at New Madrid. It was a scene repeated all along the river.

There was every kind of craft that would move on water. Every kind and description. Flatboats, keelboats, barges, arks, skiffs, canoes, pirogues. Boatmen met with shouts of recognition and glee as they shook hands and slapped the backs of old friends. New friends were made. The world was alive with talk and tales, boats and business, sounds and songs.

Boatmen, farmers, immigrants, soldiers, scouts, hunters, traders, trappers and gamblers. All were coming and going.

The "Lightfoot"

At night there were fights and frolics, color and conversation, until the silence of sleep fell while the moon rose. With the dawn came bustle and motion, new noises, new color. Sights and sounds once again, and new movement to new places.

Mike Fink was part of it all. There wasn't a man from Pittsburgh to New Orleans but what had heard of him. Not a boatman on the river but who strove to imitate him. Mike Fink. Captain of the *Lightfoot*. King of the boatmen.

7. "Dead Men Tell No Tales!"

THE *Lightfoot* skimmed down the Ohio as lightly as a dragonfly. Mike had a good pay load. In addition to the freight, there were several passengers.

Twenty miles below Shawneetown, near Hurricane Island and the Cash River, the *Lightfoot* would pass Cave-In-Rock. For many years it had been the lair and rendezvous of river pirates. The cave was high on a rocky cliff and commanded a view of the river for many miles in both directions. It had been used for years by the outlaw Samuel Mason. He had prospered in his outrages on the rivermen but had changed his place of operations to

"Dead Men Tell No Tales!"

the Natchez Trace and the lower Mississippi. Samuel Mason had fought as a soldier with distinction before he turned to a life of crime. He wanted money. Lots of it. He once said he wanted nothing but money and if he could get it without violence he would be glad to avoid shedding blood.

The infamous Harpes had used the cave. Micajah was called Big Harpe. He and Little, or Red Headed, Harpe had murdered their way through West Virginia, Kentucky and Ohio. Like Mason, the Harpes moved from Cave-in-Rock to the Natchez Trace to rob and kill the flatboatmen returning from New Orleans. Like Mason, the Harpes were captured by outraged pioneers, and were executed in Old Greenville on the Natchez Trace.

There was always danger at Cave-in-Rock. Many rivermen lost their cargoes and their lives at the hands of the river pirates. Mike Fink was determined not to be caught napping.

Once he had been. He was down in the cargo box of the *Lightfoot* when it happened. He heard the heavy sounds on the deck. The skuffling of feet. The rattle of gunfire. The shouting.

He was carrying passengers that time, too. The beautiful Aurelia Fontaine, daughter of a wealthy and distinguished gentleman, and her fiance, Maurice St. Vincent. Before Mike could scramble up the hatchway, the pirates had their prize. They had taken Aurelia.

"I'll git them, or I ain't the Snag of the Massasip!" Mike cried. He rushed to the side of the boat. The keelers followed close behind. They could see some of the bandits scrambling onto shore.

In the darkening light they could make out a small skiff in the distance. A tall man and a woman struggling. The pirate leader and the girl.

"We got to git that young lady," said Mike. "We got to teach that feller it ain't perlite to carry off a young woman against her will."

Oars were flashing now in the moonlight. The distance between the *Lightfoot* and the skiff lengthened. It was too late. They could not overtake them now.

"Give me a rifle," Mike said.

"You can't see in this light."

"It's too far."

"You might hit the girl."

There was a world of advice and warning. But no one had a better answer. It was a long shot. It was a strange rifle, not old Bang All. There was no time for preparation. No time for thought. Scarcely time to aim. The small boat was moving rapidly.

Mike Fink had shot at the shining eyes of wild animals in the blackness of the forest when his life depended on it. He had snuffed out candle flames glistening in the darkness in target shooting. His target now was a distant shadow in a moving boat. A boat that rose and fell with the irregular movement of water and oars. A dim shadow that moved in a pale silver light as the shine of the moon danced on the broad Ohio. It was like shooting a will-o'-the-wisp in a fog.

The rifle barrel became firm. Like it was frozen in

air. The moonlight skipped along its length and kissed the sights. The barrel became motionless as rock. A flash! A roar! And an echo that bounced back from the hills and trees.

There was no more flashing of moving oars. The shadow slumped forward. It did not move again.

"Got him!" said Mike.

"What a shot!" Maurice St. Vincent breathed in relief.

"None ever better," said Carpenter grimly.

"Git the girl," Mike said.

The men plunged into the water. A long, hard swim. Flashing oars again. Beautiful Aurelia Fontaine was safe. Once again she was in the protection of Mike Fink.

A year later Cave-in-Rock was infested by a new gang of boatwreckers. The new leader was Colonel Fluger, a vicious renegade who was known as Colonel Plug and hated for his ruthlessness. In common with the river pirates who had previously preyed on travelers from Cave-in-Rock, his motto and his watch word was "Dead men tell no tales." He had learned the lessons of Samuel Mason, Big and Little Harpe and the other river pirates of the past, except the last lesson. Dead men tell no tales.

Boatmen were away from home for months at a time. Immigrants on the river were far from home and friends. If Colonel Plug robbed them and let them go free, they would soon spread the news that robbers were again working at Cave-in-Rock. But if he killed them, their friends would not know what had happened to them. They might have been killed by Indians, or by storm, or by any of the countless dangers of the West. No one would know what had happened. Colonel Plug took no chances. Dead men tell no tales.

But men sometimes escaped. Slowly it became known among the boatmen that once again there was danger at Cave-in-Rock. The boatwreckers tried to get the passing boat to land. Sometimes one of their band, appearing on the river bank alone, would beg protection from pursuing Indians. Sometimes the pirates, disguised as hunters, would offer food. Sometimes they would invite the travelers to come ashore for a game of cards, a dinner, or other entertainment.

The result was always the same. Once the boat was tied up and the game or dinner started, the pirates, at Colonel Plug's signal, would pull their pistols and knives and ruthlessly murder their victims.

The boatmen banded together to protect themselves. One day the *Lightfoot* slowly overhauled Jim Wilson's keelboat.

"'Lo there, Jim," Mike shouted across the water.

"'Lo, Mike," Jim Wilson answered.

The two keelboats drew close together. "Glad to see you, Mike. I'll be glad to go with you past Cave-in-Rock," Jim said.

"I got a better idea than that. I'm spilin' fer a fight," Mike said. "An' I know how to find one."

"I ain't against a good fight myself. But I sure don't

want one with you. That red feather looks jest fine on you as far as I'm concerned."

Mike grinned with pride. "Come on over, Jim, an' we'll spin some chin music. We'll open a leetle bag of talk."

Jim Wilson jumped to the *Lightfoot* and the two men sat in the stern and talked seriously. In a few minutes they rose and firmly shook hands. They had a plan.

"Pull in to the north side," Mike directed. The two boats pulled in to shore and the boatmen gathered in two little groups along the rails of the touching gunwales.

"We got an idee," Mike said. "Six men go ahead on Jim's boat. Four men stay on the *Lightfoot*. Jim's boat will go ahead and stop under Cave-in-Rock. If Colonel Plug or his men invite you, pull up to the shore an' git off. If they ain't around, jest pull in an' tie up anyway."

As the men listened, Jim Wilson nodded agreement. Mike continued. "Then in two hours the *Lightfoot* will push off an' follow down the river. That's all. Everybody else come with me an' Jim. Have your rifles ready. Pistols an' knives, too."

The armed men jumped ashore and followed Mike into the woods. They paused on a little hill and saw Jim's keelboat turn the bend in the river. She was now in sight of Cave-in-Rock.

Jim's boat stayed close to the north shore, the dangerous side. As she came close to Cave-in-Rock, men appeared on the shore.

"Come on in," a big, red-faced man shouted.

The boat turned toward land. "That must be ol'

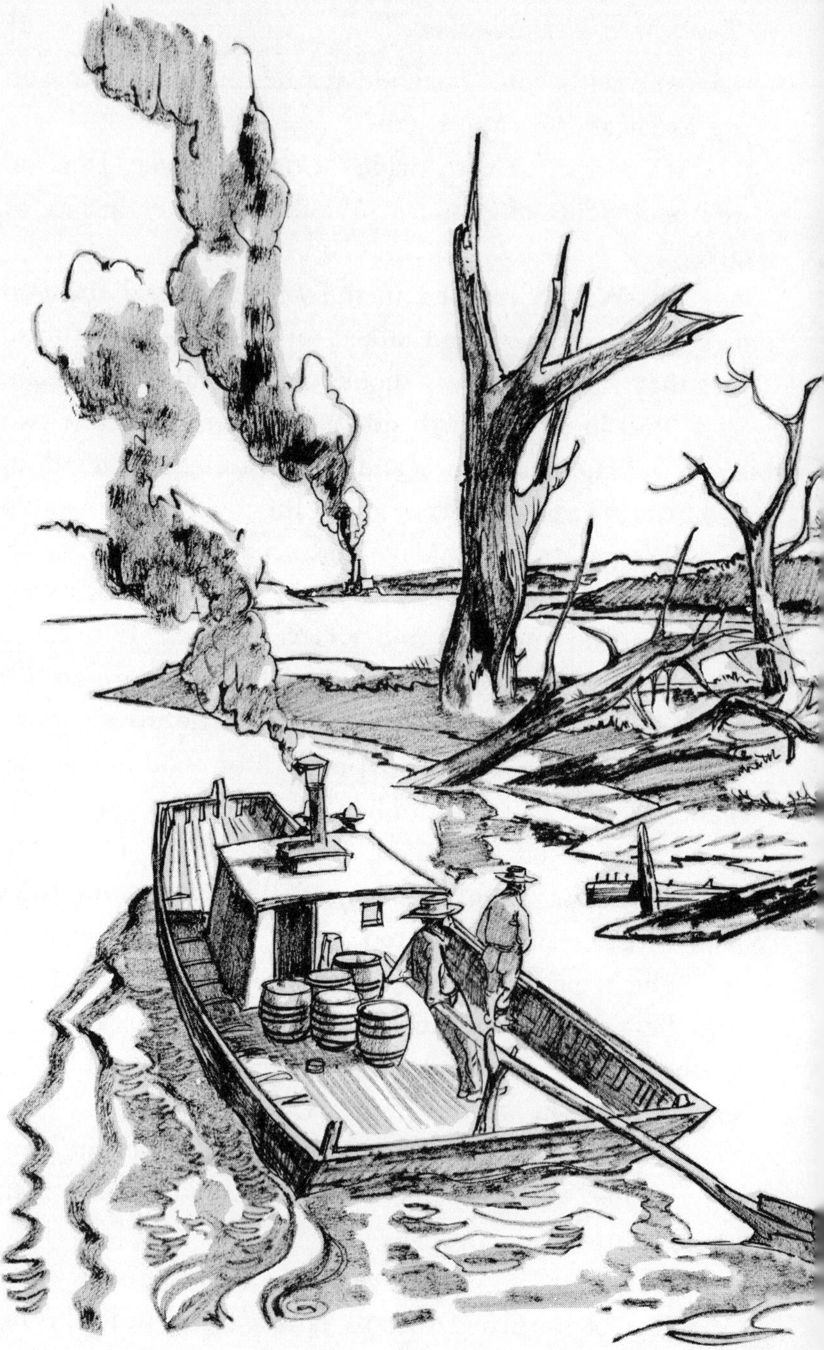

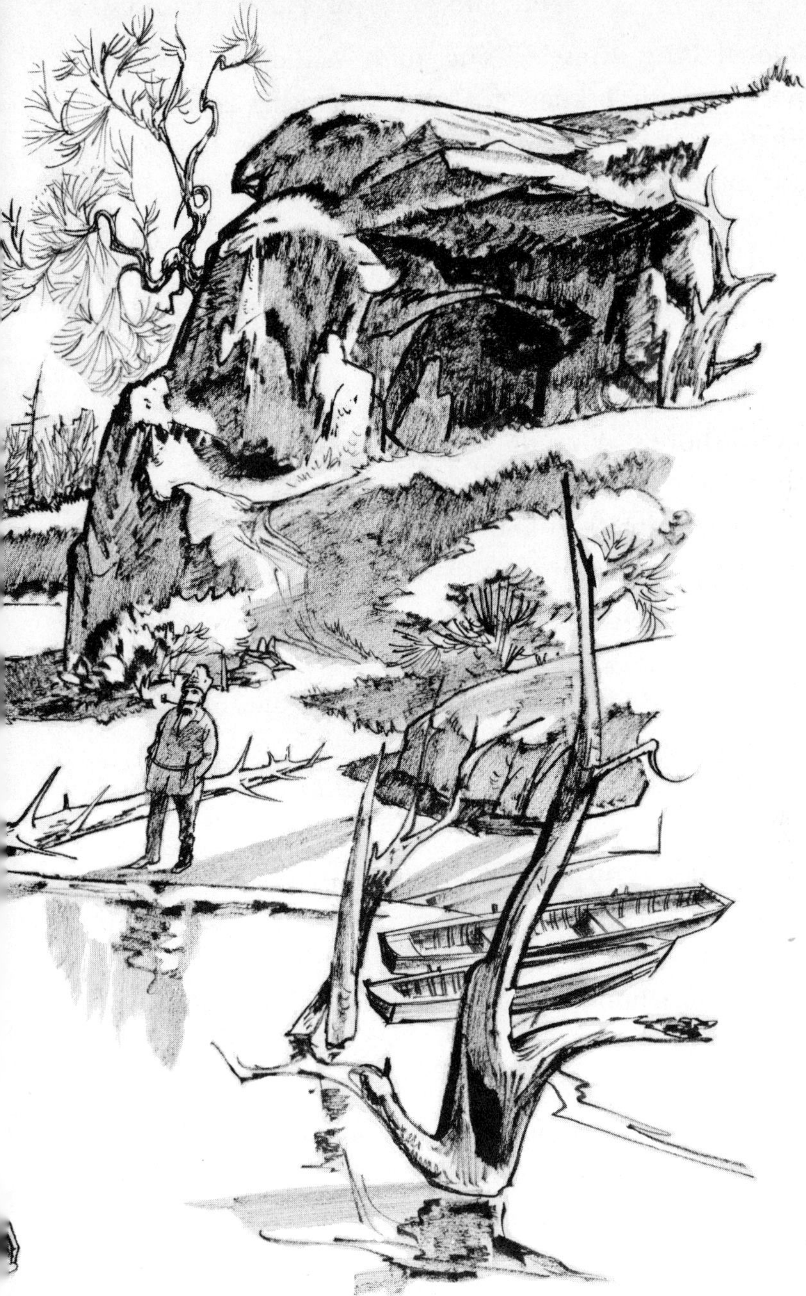

Colonel Plug himself," said John Waller, one of Jim's crew. "I wish I knew for sure what this is all about. Whatever it is, Mike didn't want the pirates to know he is around. That's why the *Lightfoot* is behind."

"Sure," said Carpenter, who had come with Waller. "If they knew Mike was around, they would run an' hide. Mebbe we don't know what it's all about, but if Mike says to do it, why, well, we'll do it."

"That's right," said Waller, as they worked the craft toward shore. "What do you want?" he asked the man on shore as the boat drew near.

"Jest wanted to know if you wouldn't like to come ashore an' have dinner with us," Plug said as he spread his fingers over the broad expanse of his soiled shirt. "Afterwards we kin have a game of cards or somethin'. We hain't had a friendly visit with anyone fer a coon's age."

"Don't mind if I do," said Waller as he tossed the line.

"Good," said Plug. He caught the rope and began to pull. "You prob'ly know all the news from up the river."

"I sure hope Mike Fink knows what he's doin'," John whispered.

"He does, even if we don't," said Carpenter.

The boat was tied and the six boatmen followed Plug to the campfire a few yards away. There were perhaps a dozen men in the clearing at the river's edge. Real hard-looking customers, Carpenter thought.

"Everybody here? All your men ashore?" Plug asked.

"Yes," said Waller.

"Only six of you, eh? Not many fer a keelboat. What you haulin'?"

"We got a special shipment of guns and ammunition. An' the usual stuff. Salt. Flax. Iron goods. Notions. Produce," Waller replied.

"Good. That's a good load. It will turn into money real easy," Plug said with a grin that showed his brown teeth through the uneven hairs of his sandy mustache.

"I expect so," Waller replied.

"But not fer you," Plug interrupted, "because we're takin' over!"

"What do you mean?" Carpenter demanded.

"Jest what I say. Are you ready, boys?" The robbers were ready. Pistols and knives were drawn and waiting.

Plug turned to his captives. His words came sharply through the brown grin. "You jest walk over there. Together. An' we'll have a little pleasant an' fancy killin'."

Under the points of the pistols, the boatmen drew together. "I wonder where Mike and Jim is?" Waller whispered.

His question was answered. "That will be about enough!" The voice was loud, but calm. It was Mike Fink's voice. Waller raised his eyes. There, at the edge of the woods, back of the pirates, were Mike and Jim Wilson and the other boatmen, rifles ready.

The pirates turned. There was a deadly silence. "At 'em, men!" Plug cried. It was the instinctive, slashing resistance of a cornered rat. There was a crack of a pistol. A rifle shot. Several of the robbers broke and ran. A rattle of rifle fire stopped them. The pirates were under control.

Mike Fink strode up to Plug. "We don't go fer this 'Dead men tell no tales.' We want some tales told. We're goin' to let you live so you kin tell other rascals it ain't safe at Cave-in-Rock. But we don't want to see this gang of yours, or you, around here any more!"

"I'll leave! I'll leave! Honest I will!" Plug stammered.

"I hope so," said Mike. "You bin preyin' an' feedin' on people long enough. You bin hidin' in this swampy country with panthers, wild cats and muskeeters, bears an' snakes. Your hide is tough. We'll jest let the muskeeters do a leetle feedin' on you so's you kin see how you like it."

They stripped Plug and his pirates and tied them to trees, their arms around the trunks. Then the boatmen took off their broad leather belts. "Keerful," said Mike. "Jest make their backs a leetle pink an' raw, so's the muskeeters will have a real enjoyable time."

Mike slapped his belt against his leg. "Who was the lookout?" he demanded. "That man who was stationed up on the hill. The one who ran away when we came up."

"There wasn't no lookout," Plug said.

"Yes, there was. An' he run away instead of comin' to help you. You kin pertect him if you want to, but I'm

"Dead Men Tell No Tales!"

goin' to make you tell me his name." Mike drew the wide belt through his hands.

Plug gave in quickly. "His name is Aaron Bowman," he said.

"Aaron Bowman. I'll remember that," said Mike as he lifted the belt and brought it down on Plug's broad back. "Remember, men," he said, "jest make 'em a leetle pink an' raw. Enough to help the muskeeters."

By the time it was over, the *Lightfoot* arrived. As he turned to go, Mike noticed that the mosquitoes had appeared in clouds and were busy at the reddened backs of the pirates. The broad back of Colonel Plug was covered with the insects. "Thicker than black bugs in spiled ham," said Mike with satisfaction.

There were other river pirates, boatwreckers and renegades. Outlaws were on the river from the beginning. Cutthroats, horse thieves, robbers. Eager to prey on others. They met on the banks of the rivers and there lived their lawless lives, attacking the boatmen and the farmers, the hunters and the trappers who were pushing west in search of homes and work.

But Mike Fink and the boatmen met them. Where there was no law, the boatmen made the law and enforced it.

They walked tall into them.

8. Mike Fink and Davy Crockett Shoot It Out

"I RECKON I'm 'bout the most modest man in the whole tarnal creation," declared David Crockett to his friend, Mike Fink.

"I ain't figgerin' to quarrel 'bout a thing like that," Mike replied softly, "but I'm all-fired modest myself."

"Take for example my shootin' with the long rifle. I reckon I never war beat at the long rifle," Davy continued. He eyed Mike carefully, marking how his words fell. "Course, Mike, I know you to be a painfully ferocious fellow—"

The implied challenge and the flattery that followed

Mike Fink and Davy Crockett Shoot It Out 89

ruffled and then smoothed Mike Fink's pride.

"And I've heerd tell that you make an almighty fine shot." Mike's pride smoothed down as soft as a contented prairie hen's back feathers.

Davy Crockett had a point to make, and he made it. The self-admitted best shot in Tennessee aimed to prove he was also the best shot on the Ohio, Mississippi and the Cumberland. "But," he said, choosing his words carefully for greatest effect, "you are a boatman. A riverman. There ain't no real reason why you should be an extra fine shot."

Mike was quick to accept the challenge. "Like I say," he said, "I'm a modest man. I reckon I'm the most modest man in the whole creation. I don't like to boast. It goes against my modest natur. But in all fairness, I got to admit that I've got the handsomest wife, an' the fastest horse, an' the best an' sharpest shootin' iron in the country, and' if any man dare doubt it, I'll be in his hair quicker than fire kin scorch a feather."

Davy Crockett turned and faced Mike. "What you say has put my dander up," he said. "I've nothing to say against your wife, for it can't be denied she's a shocking handsome woman, a horrid handsome woman. Anyway, Mrs. Crockett's in Tennessee, and I've got no horses. Mike, I don't exactly like to tell you that you lie about what you say about your rifle. But I do say that you do not speak the truth. And I can prove it."

Mike unwound his legs and stood up. He towered above Davy who was still seated on the log. "You're doin' a lot of high-powered talkin' with those real high-powered words," he said as he looked down at the famous man from Tennessee. "An' I aim to see you jest try to shoot as good as you talk."

"I'm your man," Davy replied happily. He reached for his gun and arose. He stood beside the keelboatman. His eyes ran around the edge of the clearing. A tawny wildcat ran between the trees and approached the cleared area. She jumped to the top rail of the fence around Mrs. Fink's potato patch.

"Do you see that wildcat on the fence rail?" Davy asked.

"It's a big target," Mike replied.

"It's 150 yards off," Davy answered as he expertly estimated the distance. Mike's disdain for such a large target did not prevent his nod approving the estimate of the distance.

"That varmint is listening bodaciously eager to the quack of Missus Fink's ducks waddling up the bank from the river," said Davy as he ran his hand affectionately along half the length of his long rifle barrel. "If I don't miss my guess it'll be good for the whole of creation if she loses her ears. Both of 'em. Then if she hears again, I'll be shot if it shant be without ears."

Two ears of a wildcat with one shot. Mike's eyes twinkled with anticipation to see such shooting. David Crockett raised his gun slowly, waiting for the right turn of the cat's head. He lined the sights up. The quick movements of the wildcat's head, turning first this way, then that way, to catch the sight or sound of enemy or victim presented a difficult target. An impossible target, it seemed.

"When I get them jumpin' ears lined up just perzaktly right, I'll blaze away," said Davy, "an' I'll bet you a horse, the ball will cut off both the old cat's ears close to her head, and shave the hair clean off the skull, as slick as if I'd done it with a razor."

The right moment came. The long barrel, steady as a rock, roared as Davy pressed the trigger. Mike watched, and saw the two small tufts of fur, one on each side of the cat's head, disappear. There was no doubt about it. Davy Crockett had hit his target. Both of them.

The cat heard the roar of the gun and crouched low on the top fence rail. She paused and soon slid silently to the ground.

It was a good shot, and Mike knew it. "You're makin' it desperate hard fer me, Davy," he said. "Harder than rowin' up Salt River."

The cat, convinced there was no danger, sat down on her left haunch. She lifted her right foot to her head to scratch an itching ear. Her claws, extended only slightly for personal scratching purposes, struck the place from which only recently grew an ear. It hurt. She drew her foot back and examined it. Blood!

Blood? Yes. Her own blood. She jumped four feet off the ground. She turned in mid air, yowled a frightened yowl, and bounded away into the deep woods.

David Crockett turned to Mike Fink. "The critter never knew she'd lost her ears till she tried to scratch 'em," he declared. "Talk about your rifle after that, Mike!"

Mike Fink was not dismayed. His sharp eyes sought a suitable target. "Do you see that there sow off further than the end of the world?" he asked with only slight exaggeration for the sow was a good 200 yards away. "There she is," he said, pointing with his rifle barrel. "Over there. She's got a litter of pigs jumpin' an' playin' around her. Watch the tails of them pigs."

He lifted his gun. There was a roar. The tightly curled tail of a gaily romping pig stuck out straight. "I shot the curl out of that pig's tail," he announced. He

Mike Fink and Davy Crockett Shoot It Out

was pleased with the look of amazement he saw on Davy's face.

"Now here goes some more." He loaded and fired again. Bang! Again. And again. Bang! Bang! Bang! The gun roared and each time, a curly tail shot out straight. As he put the rifle down for the last time he turned to his opponent. "Now," he said, "Colonel Crockett, I'll be pretticularly obleeged to you if you'll curl them thar pig's tails up again."

Davy had an answer. In an instant his gun was at his shoulder. Bang! The straight tail of one of the pigs was chopped off.

"It's onpossible to curl up a pig's tail with a rifle shot. But now you see that one only has a tail like a toothpick. About an inch long, I should say."

It was hard to say because the pigs had become aware of the likelihood of injury in that neighborhood. They had turned tail and were heading for the safety of the woods. Mike was resolved to end the contest in a way that would permit of no argument. "Colonel," he said, "you left that poor pig about an inch of tail to steer by. I wouldn't have done it so wasteful. I'll mend your shot."

Bang! His bullet sped on its way and cut the tail off even with the hams. It didn't even leave a nubbin.

"There," he announced with satisfaction. "You'd think that tail had been drove in with a hammer!"

Davy lifted his gun as if to reply to Mike's shot, but Mike interrupted him. "Davy," he said. "I begin to fear for Mrs. Fink's pigs. You can't shoot one off no closer. It'll prove nothin' jest to shoot another tail off close. A tail is hard for a pig to come by. But you announced it was onpossible to curl up a pig's tail with a rifle shot. Well, this is how you do it."

Each shot had added something to the pigs' steadily growing conviction that good health, long life and long tails were not to be found in that clearing on that day. They were almost out of sight in their race for the woods. Mike raised his gun. The rifle leveled off, following its moving target. Bang! A tail curled up!

"Jehosophat!" was all that Davy Crockett could say.

Bang! Another curled tail appeared. Bang! Another. Bang! Another curl.

Mike Fink and Davy Crockett Shoot It Out

"No. No, Mike," said Davy Crockett. "I can't do that. I'm sure my shootin' iron would shake in my hands if I ever thought to shoot the curl out of a pig's tail, and then shoot the self same curl back into the tail again. I'm beat, and I know it. I give up!"

Mike put his gun down. The butt of the stock rested on the ground. The long barrel ran through his hand. He gripped it firmly. Warmly. Good old Bang All. It was like shaking hands with a good, old friend. Mike smiled contentedly.

9. The Disgraced Scalp Lock

It was a beautiful day. Once again Mike Fink was on a trip down the river from Pittsburgh to New Orleans. The whole grand sweep of the Ohio and the Mississippi. From the mountains of the North to the Gulf.

The beautiful islands of the Ohio floated into his vision and slowly passed as the *Lightfoot* was carried by the even current. It was like a slow-motion dream.

Cabins dotted the river's banks. Tiny settlements snuggled under the hills and lightly touched the stream. The country was becoming settled.

The Disgraced Scalp Lock

Mike was at the sweep, guiding the craft with little effort. The crew lay nearby on the deck and the cabin top. The roughest men in the land were in a thoughtful mood. And the hardest and the hardiest of them was speaking. "I knew these parts afore a squatter's axe had blazed a tree. 'Twasn't then pulling a sweep to get a living. Pulling a trigger. Those were the times to see."

Mike had forgotten for the moment how eager he had been to get on the river. His quiet statement was followed by a pause. He took in both banks with a sweeping turn of his head. The old times had not yet entirely passed. The solitude of the Ohio could still be broken by the crack of a hostile rifle. Canoes, hidden in quiet, secret places along the shore, could suddenly dart out into the stream bent on carrying death to boatmen.

Mike's attention returned to the boat. "What's the use of improvements?" he demanded to know. "When did cutting down trees make deer more plenty? Who ever found wild buffalo or a brave Injun in a city?"

"There ain't no very big towns," said Carpenter. "Only settlements."

"But," said Mike, "they'll grow into cities. They can't help it. Here we are, thousands of boatmen, runnin' hundreds of boats. Everythin' that kin float. Deliverin' freight an' people. Oh, they'll grow all right. Farmers an' merchants an' traders movin' everywhere. They'll grow."

The pause that followed was used again to examine the banks and the boat. "Where's the fun of frolickin' an' fightin'? Gone. The rifle won't hardly make a man a livin' now. He must work. If forests continue to be used up, I may yet be smothered in a settlement."

"It's the settlements where a poor boatman can find fun an' frolics an' fights. Guess mebbe they're good fer suthin'," said Jabe Knuckles.

Mike disregarded this logic. "Nope, boys, this here life won't do. I'll stick fer a while. But I've got to have a good fight. If the Choctaws or Cherokees on the Massassip don't give us a brush as we pass along, I shall grow as poor as a starved wolf in a pitfall. I must, to live peaceable, point my rifle at somethin' more dangerous than a squirrel or a fox. Six months an' no fight would spile me worse than a dead horse on a prairie."

It was a great day for thinking and talking, but there was no time for it now. The little town of Louisville appeared. The men took their places and in a few minutes the boat was tied up.

The excitement of a new boat in town brought a crowd to the river. In the group were a number of renegade Indians. They were outcasts from their tribes. They had been expelled from their homes for some crime that shocked the conscience of their fellows or that violated Indian law. There was no place for them among the whites. They lived by hunting or trapping and stealing. They were a degraded, dissolute lot.

The hustle and bustle of the landing passed. The boatmen streamed down the gangplank and stood on the shore, surrounded by onlookers. Mike stood at the gangplank overlooking the crowd.

The Disgraced Scalp Lock

His eyes passed to the group of dirty Indians. His attention fixed on one. A tall Indian. A Cherokee who loomed head and shoulders above his companions. The tall one was facing the other way, and on his head towered a beautifully arranged and decorated scalp lock.

Mike knew that the Cherokee was very proud of his scalp lock. It was his most prized possession. To injure or damage it would be the greatest possible insult.

As Mike looked, the tall Cherokee turned toward him. "Wal, take me fer a pickled panther tail!" the big keelboatman breathed, for he saw a face that he could never forget. A corrupt and evil face, with no sign of good in it. A face he had seen years before, directing an attack against a Salt River flatboat and glaring behind a flashing tomahawk. The memory filled Mike Fink. The thoughts of revenge he had cherished flamed in him like a flash of fire.

His hand flicked to his belt and fell on his knife handle. There it paused. Killing was too good. Too quick. There was a better way. The decorated scalp lock!

Mike strode down the gangplank and up to the big Indian. He reached out his hand and plucked the hawk's feathers from the cherished scalp lock. The Indian glared horribly at Mike. The boatman calmly returned the gaze, and snapped the feathers in two. His fist crushed them, and he dropped them to the ground. Carefully and deliberately, he put his moccasined foot on the pieces and ground them into the dirt.

The Cherokee recovered his treasure when Mike

stepped back. Then, shaking his clenched fists in the air, he called on heaven for revenge and retreated with his friends.

Mike knew he had succeeded. He had inflamed the savage's soul. He had disgraced his enemy. He was pleased he had aroused so much resentment.

Talbott came up to Mike. "Mike, that's tomahawk talk. That's a bad Injun," he said. "They call him Proud Joe."

"All Injuns is bad," said Mike.

"Put 'em all together," said Talbott, "an' they won't be as mean as Proud Joe. He'll kill you sure."

"He kin try to kill me. He's already tried it once. A lot of other Injuns has, too."

Mike turned toward Proud Joe. In Cherokee and in English, he told him why he had desecrated his scalp lock. Tomahawk talk, for sure.

In English and in Cherokee, Proud Joe told Mike that he would have revenge.

"Revenge, is it?" Mike shouted. "It's revenge that I shall have. I'm from the Lightnin' Forks of Roaring River. I'm all man, save what is wildcat and extra lightnin'. I'm as hard to run against as a cypress snag. I never back water. I hold down buffalo bulls an' tear their scalps out with my teeth, an' I'll have your scalp fer what you done to me on the Salt River!"

The next morning the boatmen prepared to pull up the gangplank, getting ready to leave. Mike was at his place at the sweep. He saw the renegade Indians clustered together on a small rise a few dozen yards away.

The Disgraced Scalp Lock

The Indians hurled curses and threats at the boatman, and he responded in the manner of a boatman. "I'm the man that single-handed towed a broadhorn over a sand bar. The identical infant, the mere yearling who stripped a hickory clean by smiling at the bark. I'm sudden death to redskins, varmints meaner than rattlesnakes and wildcats!"

Proud Joe shook his clenched fist in the air and sent a thousand curses at Mike while the boatman shouted, "If any redskin denies it, let him make his will an' pay the expenses of a funeral. I'm the genuine article. Tough as a bull's hide, an' keen as a rifle."

The other Indians wandered away, leaving Proud Joe alone on the rise. The tall Cherokee stood in dark silence meditating on the cruelties he might somehow inflict on Mike.

For his part, Mike was thinking how he could further punish Proud Joe and show him up in a fair fight. As Mike watched, the Indian turned toward his companions some distance away. His head stood out boldly against the early morning sky. The impressive scalp lock, newly decorated and adorned, crowned the evil face.

Mike seized his rifle. He raised it, drew sight upon Proud Joe, and fired. The sharp retort and the shrill whistle of the bullet through space were followed by a quick movement. Proud Joe sprang high in the air, and then fell upon the ground.

A general cry of horror and indignation arose. Mike seemed surprised. Everyone knew the Indian had led the attack at Salt River, had hurled a tomahawk at Mike

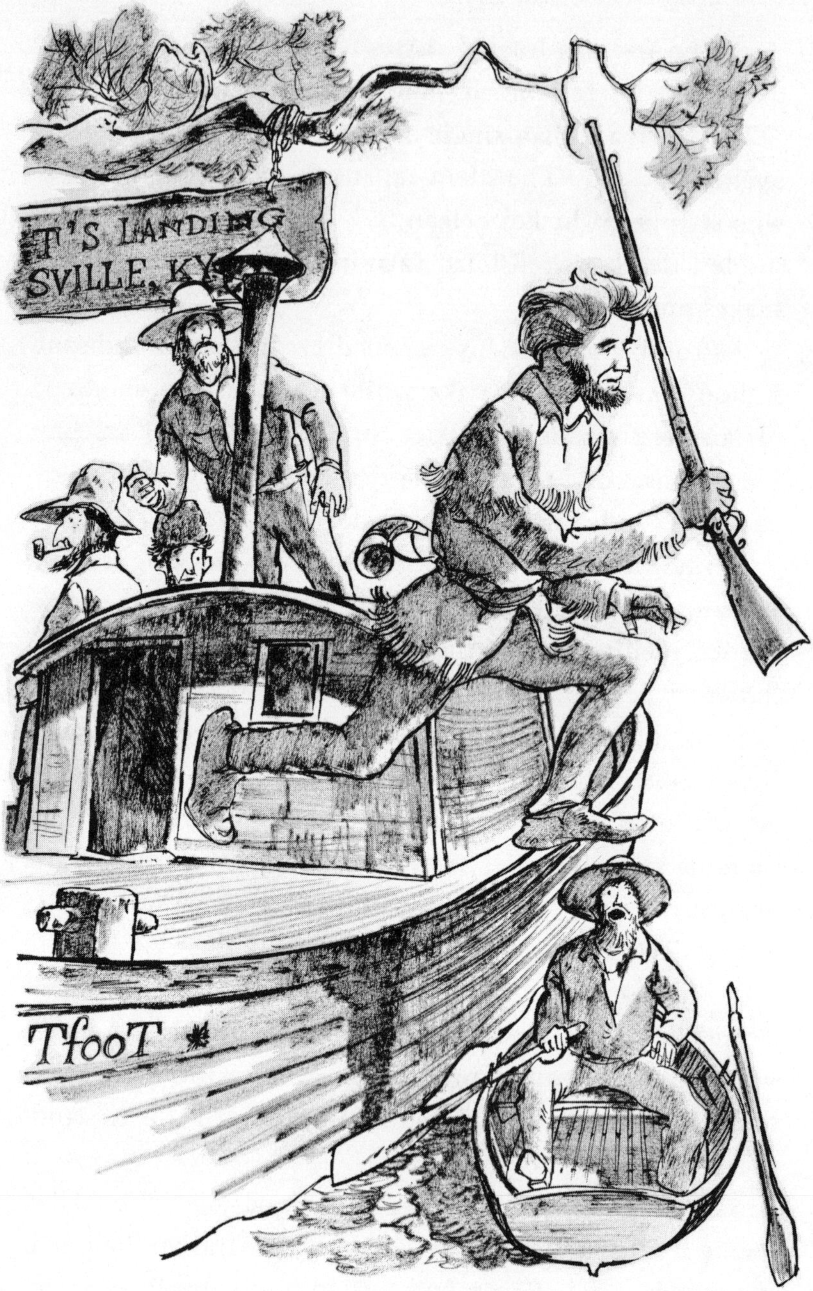
T'S LANDING
SVILLE, KY
TfooT

The Disgraced Scalp Lock

and tried to kill him. But that seemed far away from Louisville. A number of people rushed to the boat.

The boat was still tied up. Mike did not know what might happen. But he did not want to be detained. He reloaded his rifle.

"Cast off, boys," he said. "I'll see you later." He took his powder horn in his teeth. Rifle in hand, he leaped into the Ohio and began to swim with one hand. Skiffs were launched to pursue him. The men in them rowed hard. They were determined that he should not escape so easily.

The skiffs moved faster than the swimmer. When they drew near, he turned upon them. Treading water, Mike took the powder horn from his mouth.

"You think I killed that Injun," he said. "If I did, it's the first bad shot I made in over twenty years. You go back an' you'll find him alive, an' as mean as ever. I will have to kill him some day, as I have a great many others. I guess it's all right when the scouts you pay to protect your town kill Injuns in the woods. Somehow you don't seem to like the idee of Injun blood in town where you can see it!"

He returned the powder horn to his mouth. With both hands free, still treading water, he raised his rifle to his eyes. Mike's rifle, when it spoke in anger, meant certain death, and his pursuers knew it. It was true. Mike Fink didn't miss. They quickly turned their skiffs around and returned to Louisville.

10. The Revenge of Proud Joe

THE crowd on the Louisville shore watched the strange drama in the middle of the Ohio with fascinated attention. Before it was over the same crowd gaped with astonishment as Proud Joe arose from the ground where he had fallen.

They ran to the Indian in the hope of finding an explanation of the strange event. Proud Joe stood bewildered, trying to recall what had happened. At his feet lay his scalp lock. Mike Fink's bullet had cut it from his head!

The Cherokee's hair had been pulled together and

The Revenge of Proud Joe

tightly bound with a colored cord at the root of the scalp lock. The decorations, feathers and other ornaments, were held together by the cord. The bullet had snipped the treasured scalp lock neatly from the Indian's head. He had been stunned, but was uninjured.

The waterfront at Louisville was filled with exclamations of wonder and praise of Mike's marksmanship. The best shot in the West had clearly proven his prowess again.

Mike had not only succeeded in proving his marksmanship. He had succeeded far beyond his expectations in heaping ignominy upon Proud Joe. The Indian's very soul had been burned by the disgrace of having his scalp lock so taken from him.

Seize a lion by the mane. Twist a rattlesnake's tail. Pull a tooth from a wildcat's jaw. The evil and deadly reaction could not compare to that in the mind of Proud Joe. His eye glared like a fiend's. His heart throbbed with a lust for revenge. Revenge!

The crew of the keelboat pulled it into a little bay that night. The next morning they put out from shore as the sun rose. Several hours later as the river mists began to rise, the boatmen saw a column of blue smoke pointing to the sky from a fire on a point of land directly ahead. The current ran close to the point. It was an ideal place for Indians or river pirates to attack passing boats.

"If it's Injuns, I wish Mike was here with his gun," said Carpenter anxiously.

"Injuns or river pirates, that gun of his is a good one

to have around, especially if he's back of it," said Talbott.

The men were tense as the boat approached the point. Then there was a shout of relief. "It's Mike!" cried Injun Pete.

There lay Mike Fink, toasting his feet at the fire. His pillow was a huge bear. Scattered about were several turkeys and some deer. Mike was awakened by the shouting.

"Come ashore," he cried as he arose and ran to the water. A line was tossed to him. He held it while the boat turned into the shore below the point.

"You didn't kill that Injun," said Carpenter.

"No," added Talbott. "Your ball only cut his scalp lock off."

"Slick as a whistle, they said. You jest grazed his head," added Injun Pete.

Jabe Knuckles' face exploded in noisy excitement. "Didn't bring up a single drop of blood even. Best shootin' ever seen in Louisville!"

Mike seemed indifferent, but he smiled slightly. "I didn't fire at the vagabond's head. I fired at the bottom of his scalp lock. I knowed I didn't kill him. If I did, it was the first time I ever missed a shot."

The lazy days passed as the keelboat floated on downstream. The flat country of the Mississippi valley added to the monotony of the voyage. Near Natchez, in the shadow of some low hills, they pulled to shore to camp for the night. Mike was restless. Maybe it was the sight of the hills that brought back memories of fights and of Indians.

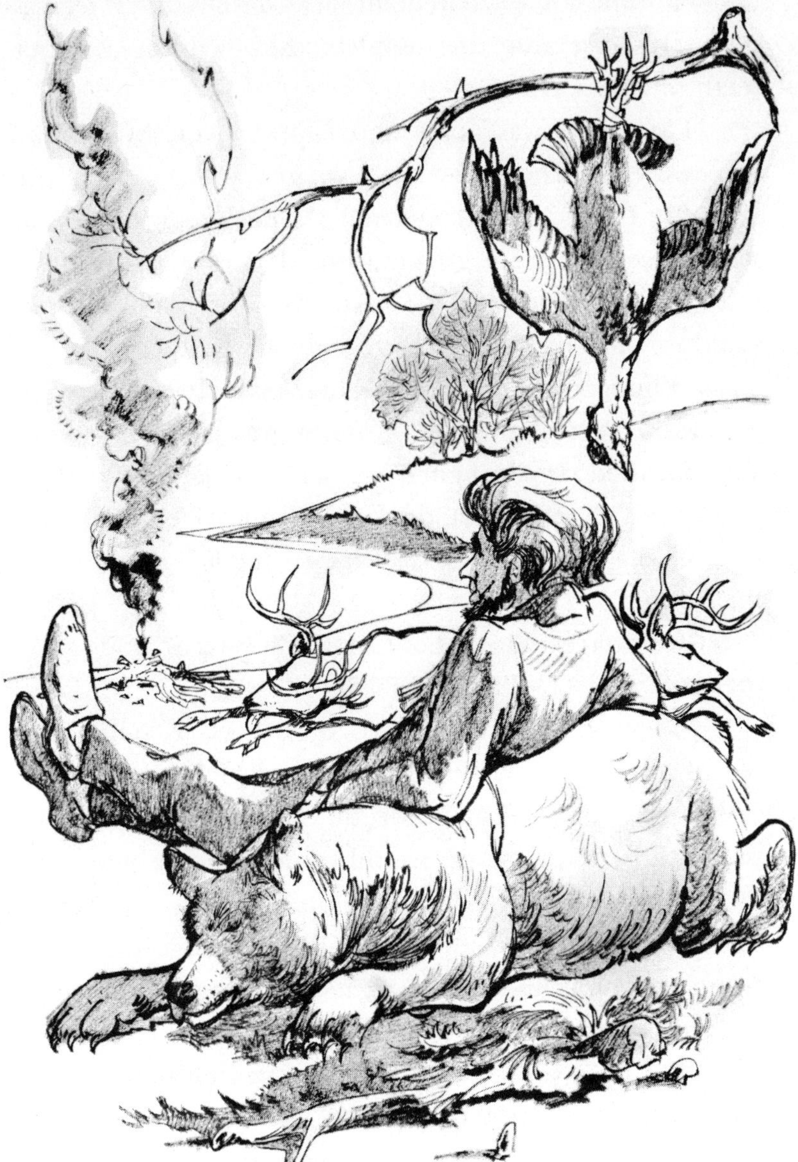

"I want some excitement," he declared. "I feel as perfectly miserable an' helpless as a wildcat without teeth or claws."

The camp was made and supper over. Still Mike was restless. "The Choctaws live in these diggin's," he said. "If I lived in these parts, I'd declare war on 'em jest to keep me from growin' dull. If I didn't, I'd git as musty as an old swamp moccasin. With my rifle I could stand on that hill there an' repulse a whole tribe."

"Them tribes come purty big," said Injun Pete.

Mike turned to him. "I never was partic'lar about what's called a fair fight," he said. "I jest ask half a chance, an' I want the odds against me. If I don't keep clear of snags and sawyers, let me spring a leak an' go to the bottom."

"Cherokees! How about some Cherokees along with them Choctaws?" Talbott asked.

"That one Cherokee, yes. An' others, too. But that one. I s'pose I got to kill him some day! It's natur that the big fish should eat the leetle ones. I've seen a trout swaller a perch, an' a cat would come along an' open his mouth an' swaller the trout, an' on the Massassip, alligators swaller the catfish. I will walk tall into varmint an' Injun. It comes as natural to me as grinnin' does to a hyena."

"I'm with you, Mike," cried Carpenter, getting into the spirit. "I'm a reg'lar tornado, wantin' somethin' to blow against. I'm as tough as hickory, an' as long-winded as a nor'wester."

Talbott joined them with a shout. "I kin strike a

The Revenge of Proud Joe

blow like a fallin' tree. I'm chock-full o' fight, an' there's no snag that kin stop me!"

Mike twirled his rifle around his head like a walking stick. "If the Choctaw devils in them there woods would give us a brush, I'd call them gentlemen. I must fight somethin' or I'll die of dry rot!"

These boasts, born of monotony, ended in a friendly free-for-all fight which was rough enough to wind up with a couple of bloody noses, some barked shins and a few black eyes. Falls were made and blows were given that would have destroyed common men. But hard fights made fast friends in the tough and rugged world where an angry fight might be the last one.

The wrestling over, the boatmen turned in. Some went below deck to the rough cabin. Some stretched out on the deck or on top of the cabin. One stayed awake to watch and guard, for there was always danger.

The moon rose high in the sky and kissed the Mississippi's ripples with lips of white gold. The cry of a startled duck broke through the even chorus of the frogs. Now and then there was a splash as a fish broke through the water.

This gentle harmony was broken by the roar of rifles and the terrifying war whoops of Indians. The guard, standing by the sweep, sank to the deck with a gurgle in his throat. One of the keelers on the deck gave a stifled groan and turned upon his face. He quivered a moment, and then was still.

The startled boatmen sprang to their feet. As they did so a hurricane of painted savages struck the boat.

There was no room and no time for rifles. The boatmen met the Indians with drawn knives and fists. Above the sounds of blows and shouts and screams Mike Fink's voice commanded, "Give it to 'em, boys! Cut their hearts out! Here's Injuns a-plenty an' they're askin' fer trouble!"

A pair of strong arms clutched him from behind. He lowered his head and tossed his assailant over it. The redskin arose, knife in hand. The white moonlight struck his face as the savage struggled to gain his feet. Mike didn't pause for a second look. The first was enough. In that short time, the time of a bullet's flight, he saw an evil face, a face he knew. It was Proud Joe!

Mike sprang, and grappled with the Indian. He was prepared for a lethal thrust when he was seized from behind. He spun around and broke the hold. Before he could again reach his enemy the redskins jumped from the boat and ran for the thicket. The attack was over.

"Hold up, boys!" Mike cried. "We can't ketch the varmints tonight, but come tomorrow an' the sunrise, Proud Joe must die!"

The fight had been short and severe. Two men and four Indians were dead. Most of the survivors on the boat had suffered cuts from Indian knives.

"Mike, look at the slices them varmints cut out of you," Carpenter said.

Mike looked at the cuts that would have killed most men. "They ain't nothin' but blackberry scratches," he said.

"Guess you got your wish about them Choctaws," Carpenter said.

"Choctaws or Cherokees, one of 'em was Proud Joe. He's follered us through the wilderness fer 800 miles. If he's so determined to kill me, I guess I'll have to beat him to it."

Mike moved to the stern where his two dead friends lay. He raised his knife toward the bright moon. "I'm goin' to desolate the nation that claims them Injuns, an' I'm goin' to exterminate Proud Joe!" he cried.

11. An Indian and a Deer

MIKE was up before sunrise and gathered his supplies together. A full powder horn and bullet bag. Some parched corn and jerked venison.

"Hang me fer bar meat if I ain't fearful glad to be on my way chasin' that dog-eyed varmint that tries to kill me every time he sees me. I figgered I was goin' to spend this whole trip doin' nothin' but sunnin' myself like an alligator on a mud bank. Now here them redskins comes an' invites me fer a brush. An' it's a good thing, too. If I didn't have one I don't know how I'd keep my jints from gettin' marrow-dried."

"I'm goin' with you," said Talbott.

"Me, too," said Carpenter.

An Indian and a Deer

"Wal, now," Mike said, "I don't know. I got old Bang All, an' I don't know — "

"I got to go," said Carpenter earnestly. "If I didn't, I'd feel as dumb as a dead pig in a mud hole."

"That's the way with me," said Talbott. "I ain't up to stayin' here. Why, I'd rather crawl into a nest of wildcats heels foremost than to have you go huntin' a dozen Injuns alone."

"Me, too."

"I want to go."

"Me, too."

The rest of the boatmen joined in an eager chorus.

"No," said Mike. "Jest Carpenter an' Talbott. The three of us with our guns loaded, an' caught wide awake is more than a match fer the whole nation that sprang down on us in the nighttime without warnin'. The rest of you stay here on the boat an' keep a sharp eye peeled. But I don't reckon they'll come back after the maulin' we gave 'em last night. That one, he might come back, but it'll be me he's lookin' fer."

Mike and his two companions were ready. They jumped from the boat to the bank and disappeared into the bushes. It was not long before they picked up the trail. "Here they go," said Mike. "Let's see. There's nine of 'em. That many ought to give us a good show, if we kin ketch 'em."

"They'll be runnin' as fast as a cat trying to git out of a rainstorm," said Carpenter.

"If we don't ketch 'em," said Mike, "I'll be as out of temper as a catfish on a sand bank."

"They're in a real big hurry," said Talbott, pointing to the footprints.

"This one here is the big Cherokee," said Mike. "If we ketch up with 'em, he's mine. I'll finish him off in less time than a Massassip alligator kin chaw a puppy."

The three men traveled awhile in silence. "Look here," said Mike as he bent down to examine the tracks. "The party's broke up."

"Yes, sir," said Talbott.

"Eight of 'em high-tailin' it off fer the north, an' one of 'em goin' south," said Carpenter.

"Yep. An' the one goin' south ought to be one of 'em that's goin' north. For it's the Cherokee. An' unless I miss my guess, the eight of 'em has got their tails between their legs an' is runnin' fer home an' safety."

"Looks that way," Talbott agreed.

"Yep," Mike continued. "But the one is goin' south. An' the reason he's goin' south is because I'm goin' south, too. He come 800 miles to kill me. He ain't goin' to give up so easy. He's lookin' fer another chance to scalp me."

"That figgers," said Carpenter.

"Now, boys," said Mike. "You two foller them eight Injuns fer a leetle while. If they stay on the trail north, an' you don't ketch 'em real soon, turn around an' go to the boat. If you do ketch 'em, no need tellin' you how to handle 'em."

"You're goin' fer the big Cherokee?"

"Right. He's mine. He wants to play, so I'll play with him. Prob'ly he'll double back. Then he'll find I'm

An Indian and a Deer

on his trail. That will give him a fair shake. Jest the two of us there in the woods, huntin' each other. Whatever killin' is to be done between us is almost bound to be done right here. If I don't git him, I'll agree to swaller a bar, tail end foremost, an' after that, I'll climb a peeled slippery elm tree heels up'ards."

"See you," said Carpenter, and he and Talbott took the trail to the north.

"We'll all start our trotters," said Mike as he crouched and slipped into the underbrush, following the Cherokee's trail.

He was right. The Indian bore south, and then turned west, toward the river. "I knowed it," said Mike to himself. "He ain't givin' up. He ain't goin' to leave till he gits me — or till I git him," he added grimly.

The Indian turned north and crossed the trail they all had taken that morning. "Now he knows there was three of us follerin' them," Mike mused.

Slowly, stealthily, he followed. Proud Joe crossed the trail Mike had made a few hours before. "Now he's caught on," Mike said. "Now he knows only him an' me is in these woods."

The Indian had the best of it, for he could stop and hide and wait. Ambush Mike. Shoot him from cover. But Mike gave him no such chance. Then, for a while, Mike was pursued by the Indian, but the savage avoided being ambushed.

Day and night the deadly game went on. They extended their field, and searched for each other through the swamp to the north, the hills to the east, and the great black forest to the south.

There could be no fire. Chew parched corn. Chew jerked venison. Chew it a long time. Make it last. Then belt soup. That would last a long time. You could go a long time on belt soup.

It rained. The trails of yesterday and the day before were gone. Still the lethal contest continued. There were long waits in the silent forest. Standing. Squatting. Lying. There were pauses for hours in the cane brakes and the woods. In a deadly game like this, a man was alert every instant.

It rained again. The search did not stop. Mike lost the Indian's trail. He was sure the Indian had lost his. A long pause. Hour after hour passed. There was no sign. The Indian had given up. He was gone. He would wait. Mike, too, would have to wait to meet Proud Joe another time.

He decided to head for the boat. Slowly. Carefully. He would take no chances. The Indian might still be around, hunting for him. You could never tell about an Indian. You could never tell about an outraged Cherokee. Mike neared the river, miles south of the place where he had left the boat.

His step was light as a cat's. Noiseless as a hawk on the wing. Soft as cottonwood down floating in air. He was skirting a burnt-out spot when he saw a beautiful buck standing at the edge of the clearing opposite him.

Mike was hungry. Terribly hungry. That deer was just what he wanted. Proud Joe was probably gone. He could risk a shot. It was not far to the river and the rest

An Indian and a Deer

of the boatmen would welcome a deer. But careful. Proud Joe would head toward the river, too.

The deer was too far away. A full 300 yards. Mike would have to get closer. He went back into the woods and circled the barren area where the deer was grazing. He was careful. He didn't want to frighten the deer. Then there was Proud Joe. No telling where he might be.

Mike drew closer to the deer. Silently. It was still a long shot. Probably too long. He should get closer. Don't step on a dry twig. Don't frighten a bird. Look everywhere. See everything. See it first.

He stopped. He melted behind a tree. Ahead, and to the left, he saw an Indian. The savage had also seen the deer and was stalking it. Mike drew his breath. It was the chance he had been searching for. The quiet, breathless, dangerous, endless days and nights were over. The Indian was Proud Joe!

Just as Mike had thought the Cherokee had left the country, the Cherokee had thought Mike had given up. And there he was! After days of hunting and being hunted, there was Proud Joe!

The deer was still too far away for Mike's shot, but it was within range of the savage's weapon. The Indian leveled his rifle at the deer. Mike Fink took aim, too. His target was in his sights.

Gunfire thundered in the silent woods. One shot, it semed. If there were other Indians around, they would think it was a single shot. But there were two shots. Proud Joe's shot at the deer. And Mike Fink's shot at the Indian. Both deer and Indian fell!

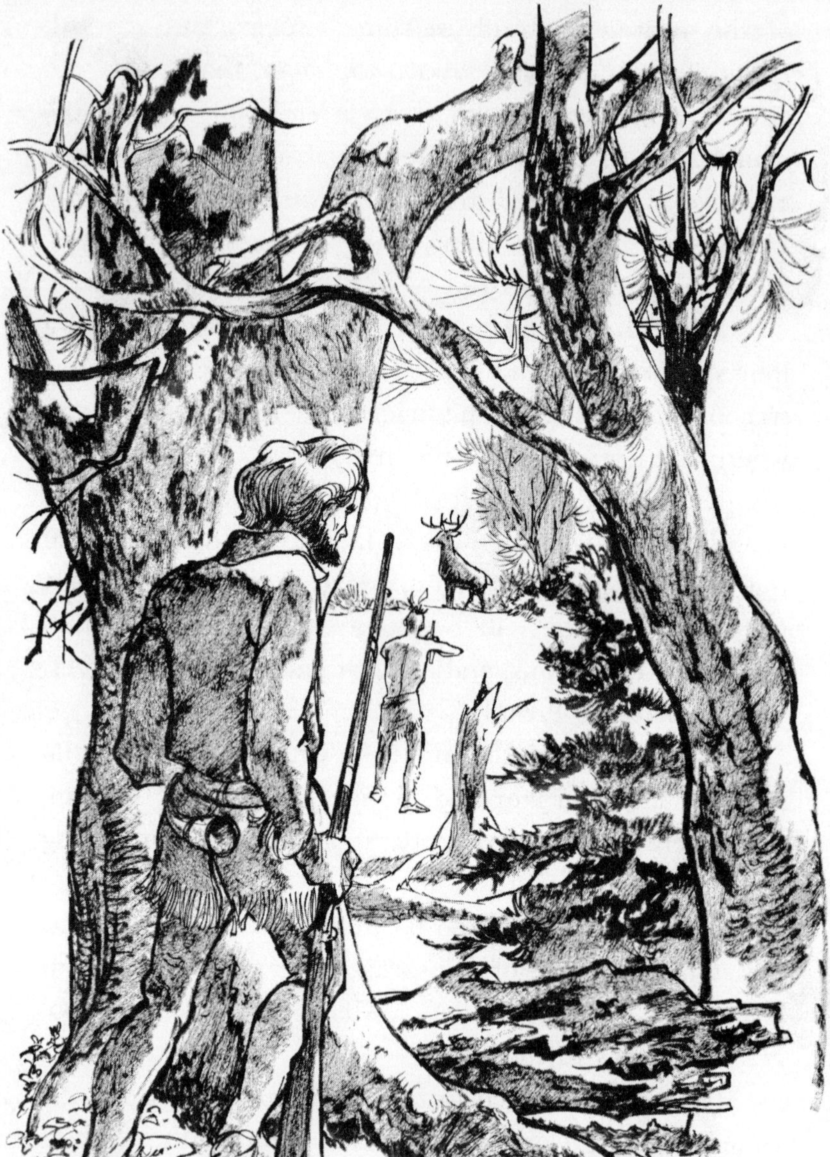

An Indian and a Deer

Mike loaded his rifle before moving. No telling what might happen. After everyone else has fired, the man with the loaded gun has control. He made his way slowly. Soon he stood over Proud Joe. Mike Fink now looked down on the savage who had once looked down on him as he threw an angry tomahawk. A Cherokee with no scalp lock. The small stump of hair that was left was stiffened with red paint. Proud Joe had sworn revenge. He had crossed swollen rivers, he had traveled hundreds of miles to avenge the fearful insult of destroying his sacred scalp lock!

Talbott and Carpenter had reached the boat several days before Mike got there. The crew welcomed Mike joyfully. They listened breathlessly as he told them of the deadly contest in the woods and how he got an Injun and a deer with one shot.

"I was spilin' fer a scrap," Mike said, "an' them Injuns gave me one. You know, I'm kind of sorry they're gone," he added, between bites of venison. "In a way an enemy is a good thing. He keeps you jumpin'. Keeps you from gettin' soft. Makes you keep your eyes open, your powder dry, your eye clear and your muscles in shape."

12. Mike Fink Enjoys Lamb Stew

ANOTHER trip down the Ohio was well under way. One fine day had followed another. Lazy days, with the sun shining warm on the deck, but yet without offensive heat. A refreshing breeze wandered over the cool, green surface of the river. It was a lazy day and it followed many lazy days.

The keelboat went with the current, guided by the long sweeping oar that acted as a tiller. No hard pole work here. Just float, eat, talk, eat. Open the talk bag, and put on the feed bag.

Mike went ashore every day or so for meat. There

was endless variety. Deer, bear, ducks, prairie chicken. Wild pigeon, rabbit, squirrel. All to be had for the taking. And taking was easy for Mike Fink and Bang All. For a change, there was fish. A pleasant hour or so with a line produced a fine meal.

Like a king passing through his domain, Mike saw the farms in the clearings along the river as they slowly slid past. The river turned and a new scene came into view. A scene of green and brown. The green of the river, the trees, the growing crops. The brown of rocks, the trunks of trees, and the earth, of plowed fields and the river bank. The green of grass, and on it — white. The white fleece of a flock of sheep grazing close to the stream in the nearing distance.

Mike's eyes, and then his mind, fixed on the sheep. They were like white balls of clouds come to earth, now floating on the green grass instead of in the blue sky. The simple beauty, scarcely recognized for what it was, magically changed into an emotion that was felt — hunger. That was what he wanted. Mutton. And there mutton was. Only a short distance away. Another man might have thought of buying it. Mike Fink might have thought of buying it another time and another place. But not now.

The current obligingly worked over to the river bank where the sheep were nibbling on the grass at the river's edge. The roof of the farmer's cabin pushed above a knoll a quarter-of-a-mile away. It was a beautiful, quiet scene. It was an open invitation for some mutton.

Mike Fink would not steal sheep. Never. But mut-

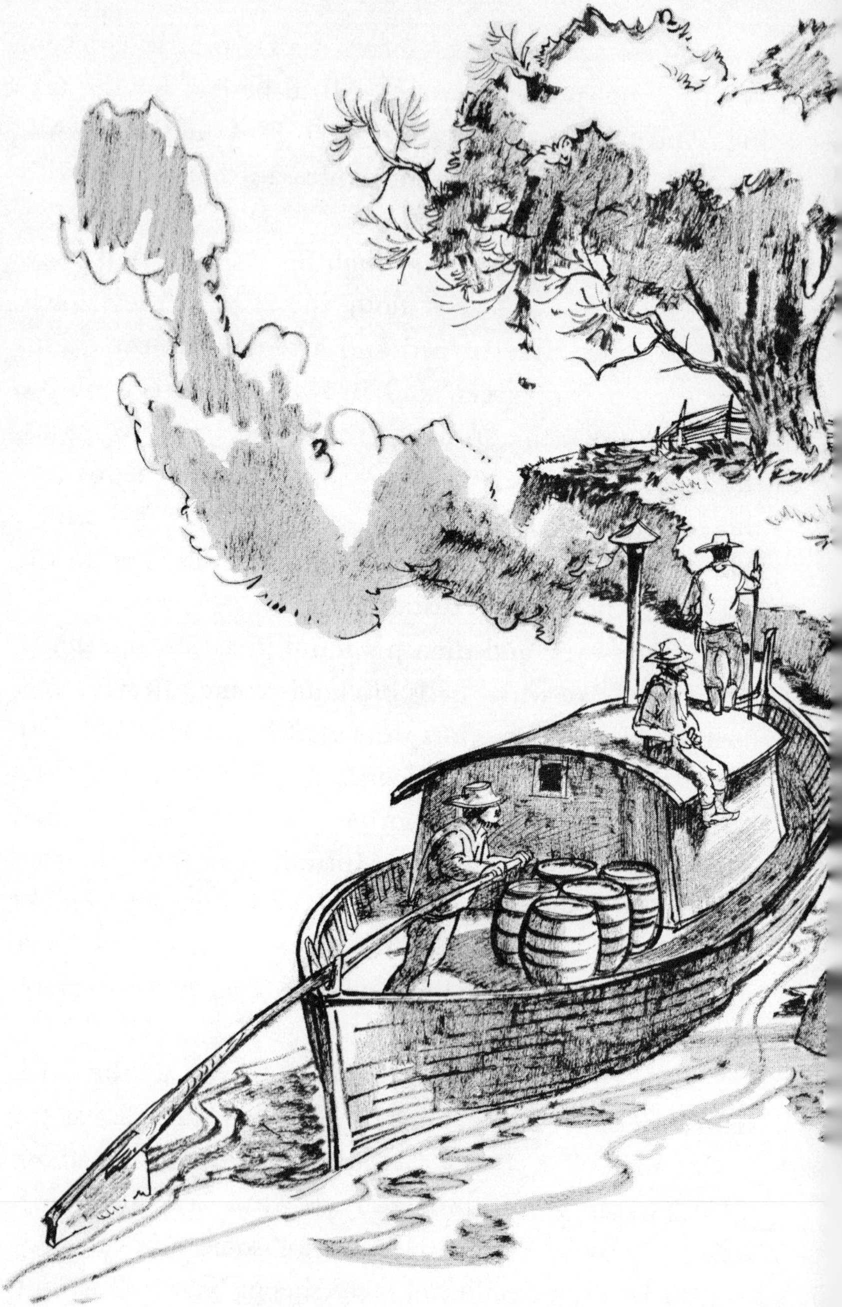

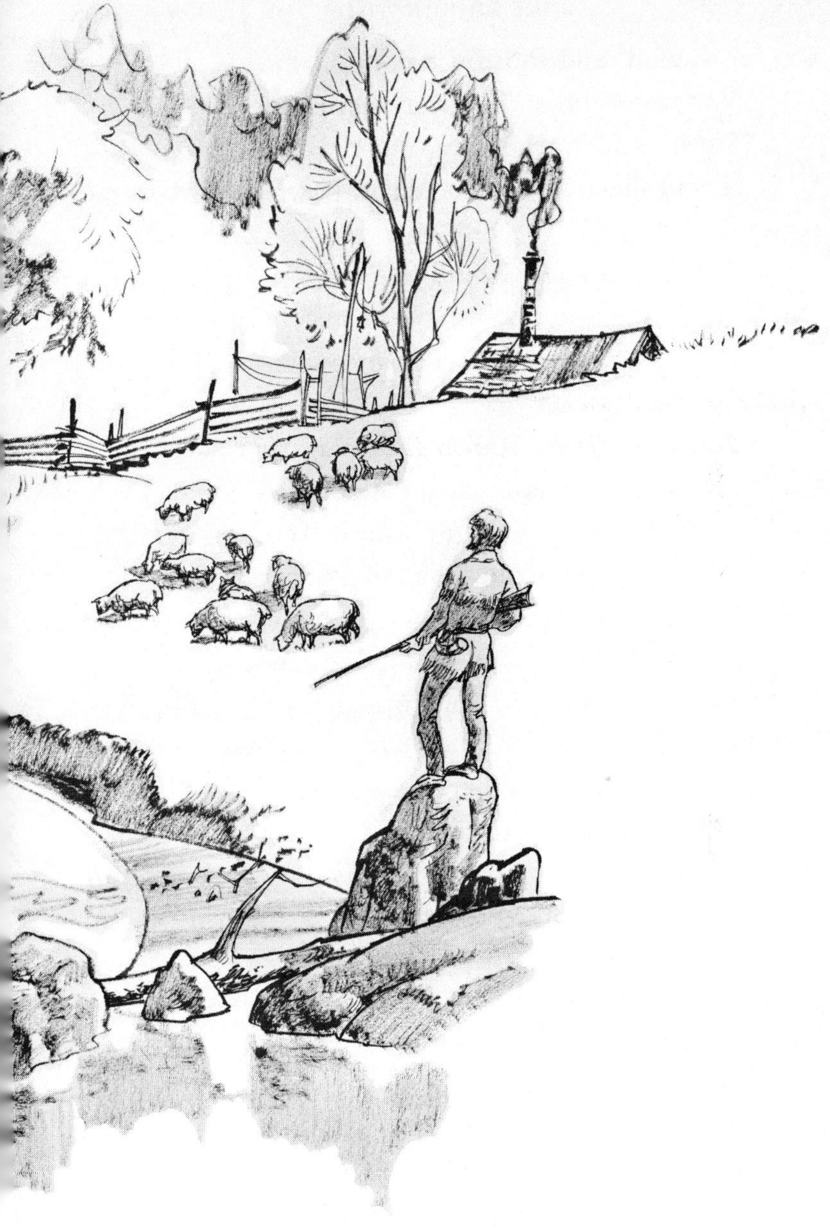

ton he wanted, and mutton he would have.

"You see them sheep over there?" he asked.

"Sure," said Carpenter. "Purty pichur, ain't it?"

"Them sheep belong to Aaron Bowman," Mike said seriously.

"Aaron Bowman? Who's he?"

"He's a creetur that ain't had his comeuppance."

"What's he need a comeuppance fer?" Talbott asked with a puzzled look.

"You ain't fergot Aaron Bowman, have you?"

"Fergot him? I ain't never met him."

"Well, I'll tell you, seein' as how you fergot," Mike said. "You remember old Colonel Plug, certainly."

"Yep. But he had his comeuppance."

"An' all his men, too," said Carpenter.

"Yep. They all had comeuppances, too. The muskeeters got a taste of them all, after our belts had their taste. They had real good comeuppances," said Talbott.

"All except one," Mike corrected. "Aaron Bowman was Colonel Plug's guard that day. He was standin' guard over Plug's camp. He was up on the hill. An' he escaped from us."

"Yeah?" Talbott's chin dropped. "How do you know?"

"Plug told me his name. Then, the last time we come through Louisville, I heard about him. He runs that farm now, and does a leetle perlite stealin' on the side. He also holds hisself out as a river pilot, and will wreck the boat of any pore traveler who might hire him.

Mike Fink Enjoys Lamb Stew

He's the feller who owns them sheep."

Jabe Knuckles who had been listening to the conversation interrupted. "Don't seem quite right that he should have all them purty sheep, an' no comeuppance."

"That's jest what I bin thinkin'," said Mike.

"Mike," said Talbott, "You got a playful look in your eye. What you goin' to do?"

Mike's reply was ready. "I bin thinkin' that some mutton would make handsome eatin' tonight," he said.

In Mike's cargo there was a shipment of Scotch snuff. Powerful stuff. He opened a package, took a handful of the snuff, and stuffed it in his leather jacket pocket. Then, picking up Bang All, his shot bag and powder horn, he said, "Edge up as close as you kin to them rocks."

Jabe Knuckles skillfully turned the tiller and the craft moved in the current toward the shore. Mike turned to Jabe. "Foller the current around the bend," he said. "Then pull in to shore an' tie up. We'll spend the night there."

"What are you goin' to do?" Carpenter asked.

"Jest don't you worry none about that," was Mike's uninformative reply. "I said I wanted some mutton, an' it's tarnation sure it's mutton I'm goin' to have. An' if I ain't too wrong, Aaron Bowman will have his comeuppance too. If I don't ketch up with you right soon, keep an eye on the river. You might see somethin' to pull out. An' not fish neither."

The keelboat floated past the rocks that projected

into the stream, and Mike jumped on to the nearest. A few more long, careful steps and he was on high, dry land.

"You're goin' to git in trouble if you steal any of them sheep," Carpenter whispered hoarsely. It was a whisper that was almost a shout because the distance between the man on the river bank and the keelboat was rapidly increasing.

"Why, Carpenter," Mike answered, "you know I wouldn't do a thing like that. I won't do hardly anything Aaron Bowman don't ask me to."

As the keelboat passed around the bend in the river and out of sight, the men saw Mike approach the sheep. They were fat and young. This would not be mutton. Nothing so common. Lamb, it was.

It was no trouble for Mike to catch several of the animals. When he did, he rubbed their faces vigorously with the snuff. Then he hurried over the knoll to Bowman's cabin. He found that gentleman carrying some corn to feed his hogs.

"Is them sheep over the hill there yours?" he asked excitedly.

"Reckon so," the farmer replied.

"You better go an' look at 'em powerful' quick," Mike said in a voice that revealed the need for desperate measures.

"Why?" Bowman asked with concern.

"Come on!" Mike turned. Bowman followed and caught up with the riverman. The urgency was clearly very great, and soon both were running.

After they passed over the brow of the hill and came in sight of the sheep, the reason for their speed and for Mike's concern became clear. Some of the flock were strangely affected. They were leaping and bleating and rubbing their noses against the ground. They were pushing their faces in each other's wool in a very unsheeplike manner.

"What in tarnation's name is the matter with them sheep?" the farmer shouted.

Mike looked at the affected animals sagely. He pursed his lips and shook his head sadly. His reaction made it apparent that whatever it was, it was very, very bad indeed. "Seems like it's mostly the fat lambs that's ailin'," said Mike.

"Do you know what's the matter with my lambs?" the farmer asked. His voice was quiet and serious now.

"Don't you know?" Mike answered grimly.

"No. I never seen nothin' like that before."

Mike lowered his voice. "Did you ever hear of the black murrain?" he asked somberly.

"Yes!" was the terrified reply. The horrible thought of the dread disease brought to the sheep owner's mind an appalling picture. Every sheep, every animal dead!

"That's what it looks like to me," said Mike. "The black murrain. I've heerd about it all up an' down the river. Sheep up the river have it dreadful. Dyin' like dogs. Thousands a day. Whole flocks wiped out."

"Ain't there no cure fer it?"

"Well, the murrain's dreadful ketchin'. If you don't git rid of 'em that has it, it'll spread through the whole flock. Git rid of 'em right away. Don't waste no time. That's what everybody says. They got to die, anyway." He looked at the distressed sheep as they rubbed their watery eyes and running noses against whatever they could manage to reach. The earth, bushes, each other.

The terrified owner saw the poor animals dancing about and running erratically. "But how kin I ketch 'em?" he cried desperately.

"Why do you want to ketch 'em? You might git the black murrain on your hands. It would seem to be better to shoot 'em."

"But I couldn't hit 'em. I ain't got my gun here. Nobody could hit 'em, the way they're runnin'. He might hit the ones that ain't ketched it yet."

Mike shifted his weight and drew himself up straight. "My name is Mike Fink," he said simply.

That was enough. Everyone on the river knew of Mike Fink. Here was the best of all marksmen. Just the man for such a job. If Aaron Bowman had ever returned to Plug's camp, or if he knew it was Mike who had cleaned out Plug's gang, he didn't show it.

"Shoot 'em! Please shoot 'em," he urged. "You kin pick off the sick ones."

"It might be a mistake," Mike said cautiously. "They might git well."

"No, they won't. They can't," was the distressed reply. "Look at 'em. No sheep of mine ever acted like that before."

"I don't quite like to go around shootin' sheep. You

Mike Fink Enjoys Lamb Stew

best call some of your neighbors an' ask 'em if it's murrain sure 'nuf."

"No one else but you could hit sheep that is jumpin' around like that." The farmer watched Mike intently. Perhaps flattery could overcome the famous marksman's foolish scruples.

"Wal, now — "

That was it. Flattery. It was easy to see that Mike Fink would perform this impossible task if he were flattered. "I never seen you shoot," the farmer said. "I always wanted to see the best shot on the river in action."

"But I don't think I ought to — "

"I'll pay you," the desperate sheep owner urged. "I'll pay you well.'"

"I don't like to take money fer doin' a man a favor," said Mike. "But if you got a few fresh vegetables — "

"I have. I got lots of 'em. Carrots, parsnips, cabbages, potatoes, turnips. Everything."

"Onions?" asked Mike.

"Yes. Oh, yes. Onions, too," said the farmer. "And I kin give you a gallon of peach brandy."

"Wal," said Mike thoughtfully. The farmer held his breath while Mike meditated.

"I wouldn't like to do a thing like that for money," Mike said at last. "But to help a mannee out — wal — all right. But I got quite a few men on the boat to feed," he added cautionsly.

"That's all right," the sheep owner insisted. "I want you to take all the vegetables you kin carry."

Thus persuaded, Mike quickly shot the affected sheep. "There," he said, "that's five of 'em. That seems to be all that's got it."

"No. I think there's another. There. That one!" the farmer said, pointing.

"No. That's enough," Mike replied. "Only five of 'em was actin' up, an' I got 'em. That one. She ain't got it — yet. Only five. She's a leetle too old, I think."

"Are you sure?" the man asked. "Shouldn't we ought to play safe?"

"No," Mike answered. "Only five, I think."

"Thank heavens," said Bowman. "Now I'll go git a spade so I kin bury 'em."

"I'd be keerful about that," said Mike quickly. "If you should bury 'em, you'd still have the murrain right here on your place. No tellin' what might happen."

"What will I do?" asked the harried man anxiously.

"Wal, if I was you, I'd sorter think 'bout pushin' 'em in the river."

The man brightened. It was obviously a good idea.

"Then," Mike continued, "the black murrain, if they has it, will go 'way off, down the river. An' I don't s'pose you keer what happens down there."

It was a fine idea! Of course Aaron Bowman didn't care if the disease was carried down the river. "That's right," he said brightly.

"That way you won't have to git a spade an' do any diggin'. I'll tell you," said Mike cheerfully. "You go an' git the vegetables, an' while you're gone, I'll jest drag them sheep to the river an' push 'em in. By the time you git back, with the vegetables, the sheep will be gone, an' you won't even have to touch 'em."

This was the fulfillment of everything Bowman could have asked for. He hurried over the hill, and soon returned struggling under a burden of an enormous load of vegetables and a gallon of peach brandy.

Mike Fink was as good as his word. He had disposed of the sheep, and the satisfied farmer sighed with relief as he saw the five wooly, white objects floating away on the smooth surface of the Ohio River. "Here's the vegetables," he said as he shifted his heavy burden into Mike's strong arms. "An' here's the brandy. An' I'm all-fired, bodaciously, everlastingly grateful."

"It wasn't nothin'," said Mike casually. "I was dreadful glad to do it fer you. My men is tied up to the shore down the stream a leetle ways. I'll ketch up with 'em in no time." He shouldered his load and turned away.

Mike melted into the woods toward the southwest. In a few minutes he caught up with his men who had tied up just around the bend. In a few more minutes, with the help of Carpenter and Talbott, he pulled the five fat lambs out of the river as they came floating down the stream.

"I hope Jabe an' Injun Pete ain't wastin' no time gettin' the vegetables ready," said Mike, "because I'm ready fer some of Aaron Bowman's lamb stew."

13. Mike Fink in a Tight Place

THE *Lightfoot* floated easily at her moorings. The moon was still low in the sky. The songs and stories had been sung and told. It had been a wonderful evening. Davy Crockett was there. Whenever Davy Crockett was around the tales were good.

Suddenly Carpenter said, "Mike, ain't you ever bin worsted in a scrap?"

"Yep. Ain't no one never whipped you?" asked Injun Pete.

"Nope. Not as I remember. I never backed away from anythin' that travels, from a Massassip gallinipper

Mike Fink in a Tight Place

up to an alligator. I guess I have drunk so much river water that I'm jest chock-full of sand bars, snags, rafts, and sunk flatboats, an' nobody kin whip me," said Mike.

"I know you beat me with a long rifle, but now I got to say I doubt that you're speakin' the truth," said Davy.

Mike shot a quick look at him. "But mebby not," Davy added. "I guess no *body* ever whipped Mike, but some *thing* has. An' only last Sunday, too."

Mike's stern look spread out into a grin. "I guess that's right," he said. "I didn't intend to say much about it. But that's right. I gave in once. An' only last Sunday at that."

"Tell us about it," Carpenter said.

"Ask Davy," said Mike. "He seen it. He was swimmin' nearby an' he seen it all."

"Wal," said David Crockett in his best story-telling manner. "It's worth tellin'. You may talk about your scrimmages, tight places an' sich like, but Mike was in one that was what you might call a real tight place."

"I've fought all kinds of varmints," said Mike, "from an Injun down to a rattlesnake an' never was willin' to quit fust, but this once."

"It war an awful hot day, an' Mike was near runnin' off into pure ile. He come to the crick in Deacon Smith's medder an' figgers a dip would save him," said Davy.

"I unharnessed in the bushes. Got my pants an' shirt off an' was standin' in my birthday clothes. First birthday, that is. I hauled my red shirt over my head an' slung it on the bushes an' swum across the crick."

"Then Mike looks up an' he sees Deacon Smith's

ole brindle bull makin' a bee line fer that red shirt," said Davy. " 'Course everybody knows how that ole critter has scared all the persons in the settlement, an' come mighty near killin' a few."

"Thinks I, 'Mike, you're in rather a tight place. Git your fixin's on or he'll be drivin' them big horns through you,' " said Mike.

"So Mike didn't have no time," said Davy. "The bull war on one side of the crick an' Mike war on t'other, an' the way that bull war pawin' an' stompin' an' makin' the sile fly as if he war diggin' Mike's grave, war real distressin'. He pawed and shook his horns at Mike's clothes. An' by gravy, somehow those clothes got caught on that bull's horns. Pants, shirt and drawers wavin' away like flags on the fourth of July!"

The keelboatmen grinned and Mike shook his head soberly as he recalled his predicament.

"Mike was plumb nekkid," said Davy. "Didn't have time to think hardly. But he's got a lot of fight as everyone knows, so he yells out, 'Come on, ye bellerin' ole beast, an' don't be standin' there, fer ye ain't purty!' "

"This here statement somehow reached the bull's understandin'. He bellers a little. He hoofs a little. An' he makes a dive. Right across the crick he comes. Mike don't aim to stand in anybody's way, so he gin him plenty of room. The bull passed him an' does a 'bout face fer another charge."

"I wasn't skeered," said Mike. "But I was bein' real keerful."

"Yep," said Davy. "So Mike makes up his mind an'

Mike Fink in a Tight Place

is ready the next time. When the bull charged again, with Mike's clothes still wavin' in the breeze, Mike grabbed his tail an' got pulled up the bank. Then ole brindle started comin' 'round again, an' Mike pulled his tail t'other way."

"That sort of riled him," said Mike. "He jest looked at me disgusted like. Then he commenced pawin' an' bellerin' again, an' the way he made his hind gear play in the air was beautiful!"

Davy spread his hands out to aid in the telling. "But he couldn't touch Mike, the way he jumped around. So Mike made up his mind he would stick to the bull's tail, as long as the bull's tail stuck to the bull, and as long as his clothes stuck to the bull's horns. He didn't want to yell fer help because it war against his principles. Anyway, he couldn't. Y'see, the Deacon had jest preached a sermon in his house, an' the hull congregation war there, an' would come a-runnin' out."

"I most certain sure didn't want all them ladies at the preachin' to come out an' see me in that there predicament," Mike said, as the keelboatmen laughed uproariously. "So I says to that ole sarpent of a bull, 'Do your worstest!'"

"An' he did!" Davy roared. "The bull starts to runnin', kickin' all the way. He drug Mike over every briar an' stump in the field until he war a-sweatin' an' breathin' like a fat bar with a pack of hounds at his heels. That ole critter went so fast that Mike, hangin' on his tail, blowed out dead level with the varmint's back! Mike's clothes was still on the critter's horns, flappin' like willer trees in a hurricane. When he finally stopped a little, Mike dropped behind a stump an' snubbed the critter with his own tail!"

" 'Now there,' I says to the varmint, 'you'll either pull up this white oak stump or break your tail,' " said Mike. " 'Or else you'll jest hold in a bit till I blow an' git my breath!' "

"What happened?" Carpenter shouted.

"Go on! Go on!" cried Talbott.

"Go on!" echoed Davy. "That's right! But how? Mike had the bull by the tail, an' he couldn't let go. If he let go an' run, the bull would be afoul of him sure. That bull war mad. He blossomed out like a punched painter."

"I come to the conclusion I'd better let someone know where I was," said Mike. "So I yelled. Louder than a boatman's horn. I thought I might git some help which I needed real bad."

"I was watchin' from a branch," said Davy, " 'bout a quarter mile t'other way from the house. I had been takin' a dip, too. I had washed my clothes an' I didn't have my gun. There wasn't nothin' I could do but try to dress in my wet clothes as fast as I could, and go to the house fer help, or a gun, or somethin'. But when Mike yelled fer help, no people came. Only two more critters. The Deacon's two yeller houn' dogs. Well, they wouldn't be no help fer Mike. They'd join the bull. They war awful wenemous, an' had quite a spite against Mike."

The excited roars of the boatmen split the night and drowned out the noise of croaking bullfrogs.

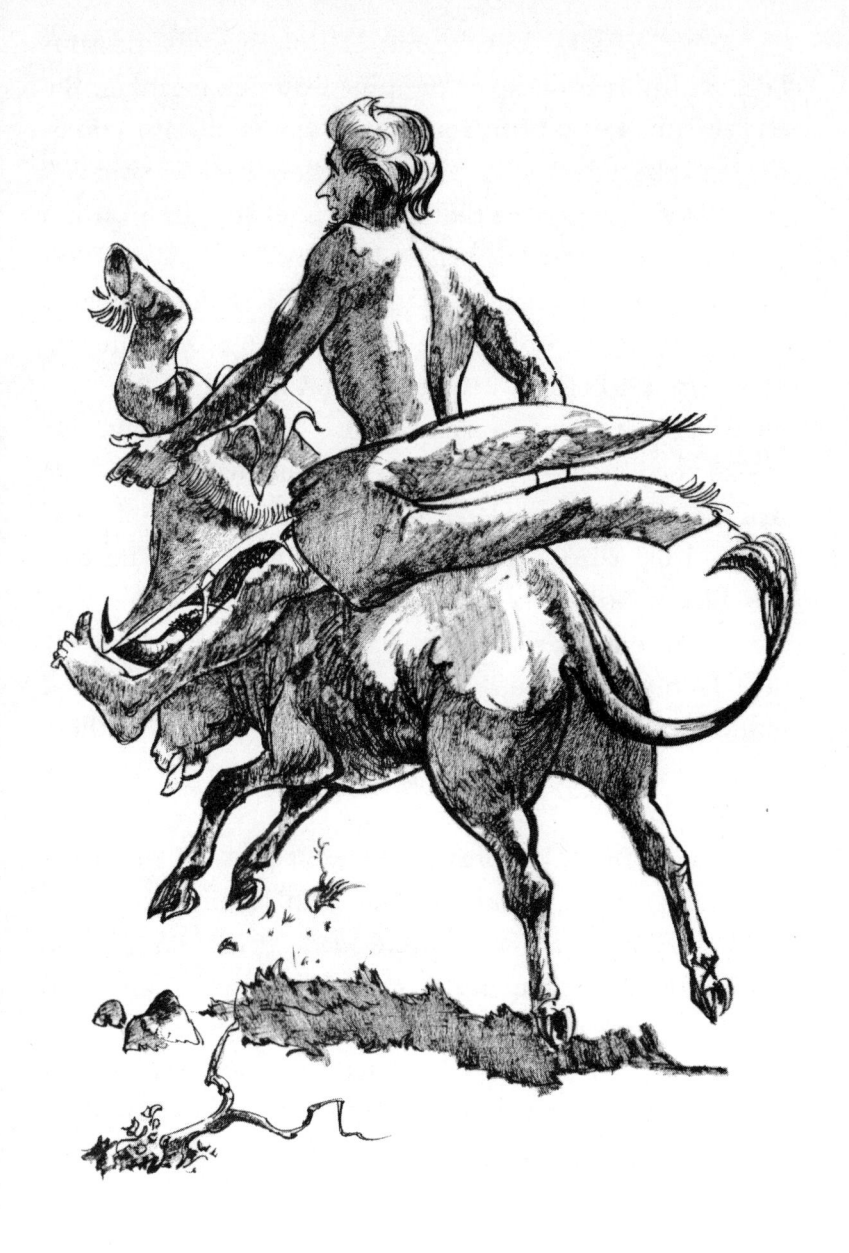

" 'So,' says I," Mike shouted, " 'ole brindle, do your best. Ridin' is as cheap as jumpin' around hangin' on the end of your tail on this route, so if you've no objections, I'll jest take a deck passage on that there back of yours!' "

"Mike got aboard that critter quicker than a cat kin bat his eye," Davy continued. "You'd of sworn thar warn't nothin' human in that thar mix. The sile flew as the critter rolled around the field, a dog on each side, an' Mike tryin' to clinch his feet around the beast. No matter what that bovine varmint done, Mike stayed on. He was as good a cowboy as he is a keelboatman. He rid ole brindle till the beast decided to take in a supply of wind an' cool off a little and stopped under a tree. The bull was blowin' like a winded porpoise."

Mike couldn't wait for Davy to continue. " 'Now,' saye I, 'ole boy, you'll lose one passenger sartin.' So I clumb on a branch of the tree, calc'latin' to roost there till I starved, afore I'd be rid around that there way any more."

Davy caught his breath and went on with the story. "The dogs were barkin' an' showin' their teeth in a most unfriendly manner. Mike made tracks fer the top of the tree. But he heard somethin' makin' an orful buzzin' overhead. He looked up, an' if there warn't — well, thar's no use swearin' — but thar was the biggest hornet's nest ever built!"

He slapped his hands on his knees and before he could catch his breath, Mike continued. "I says to myself, 'You'll give up now,' says I, ' 'cause there's no help fer you.' But then an idee struck me. Thinks I, 'You'll

Mike Fink in a Tight Place

have a heap better chance *ridin'* the ole bull! Besides that he's still got my clothes stuck on his horns.' Anyway, how do you give in to a bushel of mad hornets? So I jest dropped aboard the bull again an' looked aloft to see what I'd gained or lost. Well, sir, I'm a liar if there warn't half a bushel of the stingin' varmints ready to pitch into me when the word 'go' was given!"

Davy took up the story. "Some one must of give the word, 'cause all hands started down. A bushel of hornets, all mad as hornets, with fire in their eyes, and their stingers sharp and ready. Some of 'em bit the dogs. About a quarter of 'em struck Mike, an' the rest charged ole brindle! The dogs lit out first fer home, yippin' an' hollerin' like a dozen steamboat whistles all out of control. Ole brindle follered quick an' went so hard Mike couldn't steer him. The hornets follered. The dogs was yelpin' loud as a wildcat hollerin' fer mercy. Ole brindle was a-bellerin' like a buffalo bull stuck in a bog. An' the hornets was a-buzzin' an' stingin' — like hornets. Mike didn't say nothin', fer it war no use. He wasn't doin' no river-screamin' at all. Everything else was makin' the noise, an' talkin' real tall, too!"

The keelers shouted with excitement. Davy Crockett took a deep breath and went on. "About 200 yards from the house they war, when the Deacon heard the ruckus an' come runnin' out. He jest held up his hands and turned pale. The hull congregation, men, women an' chlidren, come out after him, an' they all started yellin'.

"Ole brindle was runnin' real serious. The hornets were keepin' up easy. He couldn't turn from a fence that stood dead ahead. When he reached the fence, he stopped short. Mike didn't stop, an' went ashore. He floated over the critter's head an' over the fence, an' out! His clothes, all punched full of holes, come sailin' after him."

"The men come to help me," Mike added. "An' the women, noticin' my lack of clothes, beat it back into the house fer modesty's sake. I'm still some sore. An' my hornet stings, while they ain't so swollen, is still with me. An' I got to admit, Mike Fink had the worst of a scrimmage once in his life!"

14. Mike Fink's Trip to Court

THERE was not much law on the western frontier in Mike Fink's day. But a court was established at Louisville which was then a rapidly growing town of several hundred inhabitants.

It was difficult to keep a constable. When the constable failed to make an arrest and bring an accused person into court, he lost face, and became ineffective as a law enforcement officer. Public clamor and criticism soon brought about his resignation.

Mike, in common with many active men, had enemies. His exploits often made many people laugh, but they made others angry. His work often brought him to Louisville. He came and left suddenly and without notice.

His little tricks, as he called them, usually brought a smile to those who were not their victims. He got credit for a great many little tricks he did not perform, and he no doubt performed some he didn't get credit for. In any event, he became a wanted man by the court at Louisville. The reason is not certain. It may have been because of complaints by Aaron Bowman. It may have been because of Proud Joe and his scalp lock. It may even have been the work of friends of Colonel Plug.

No Louisville constable had been able to bring Mike into court. Several had tried, and failed. Naturally, after their failures, they had resigned.

Big Jabe Knuckles had broken his leg, and had stayed in a cabin on the outskirts of town until he could get around again. He was a good man with his fists, a club or a gun, so he was asked to take over the constable's post. It became his duty to bring the big riverman into court.

Soon after, Mike's keelboat tied up at Louisville. To fulfill his duty Jabe Knuckles went down to the river and sought out the *Lightfoot*. As he approached the boat, Mike, standing at the stern, saw him. "Why, Jabe, you ole 'possum, how are you?" he shouted.

"Fit as a fiddle. An' as spry as any critter with a leg an' a half ought to be," Jabe shouted in reply.

"Come aboard! Come aboard!" Mike yelled.

Jabe climbed on the boat and the two men shook

Mike Fink's Trip to Court

hands vigorously, shouting and laughing as they slapped each other on the back.

The news spread that Mike Fink was in town and the new constable was going to try to take him to court. A crowd gathered. This would be fun. It always had been.

Jabe was not long in breaking the news. "Mike," he said. "We bin good friends fer a long time, ain't we?"

"Sure 'nuf. Enormous good friends. We worked the river together. We pushed a pole together. Best of friends."

"An' you know, Mike, I got a big family."

"That's right. A big family. A fine family. Mrs. Fink an' my daughter Sal always speak most kindly after 'em."

"An' if I don't bring in money regular, they go hungry."

"Right as rain."

"That means I need a job," said Jabe plaintively.

"You kin have a job. You kin have a job on the *Lightfoot* any time you want it," said Mike.

"But I ain't got two good legs yet."

"Mebbe I kin find somethin'," said Mike cordially.

"No, I can't do work on the river without two good legs. Anyway, I got a job," said Jabe hesitantly.

"Fine! That's real good. What you doin'?" Mike asked.

Jabe hesitated. Then he boldly plunged ahead. "I'm the constable here," he said.

"Fine! Always be on the side of the law. That's

what I always say. I hope you do a good job. I know you will. I do wish you dreadful good luck," said Mike. "Be sure to let me know if I kin help you. I never like to fergit a friend."

Such an offer was too good to be true. Jabe seized at it. "You kin help me. You kin help me right now," he said.

"How?" Mike asked.

"Let me take you to court," Jabe replied.

"What?" Mike exploded.

Jabe rushed into explanations. "You know I got a big family. I need this job till I git two good legs again. If I don't take you to court, I won't have a job. If I do take you to court, I'll git a reward, most likely. It'll pay the doctor. Winter's comin'. The kids need clothes. I got to have it!"

"Wal, now — "

"Nobody kin really convict you of anything. Anyway, if they do, you kin escape easy. I know you got a kind heart. You wouldn't want to do me no harm," Jabe pleaded.

Mike scratched his head. He was deep in thought. "I see your point, an' like you say, I'm an obleedgin' somebody. So I'll do it!" Jabe sighed with relief.

"But on one condition," said Mike.

"What's that?" asked Jabe.

"I'm on a boat so much I don't feel at home nowheres else," said Mike.

"But it won't be for long."

"No. I don't want to leave my boat. An' I don't

Mike Fink's Trip to Court

want to leave my men," Mike said firmly.

"But, Mike —"

"So I'll tell you what we'll do. You take me an' all my men in a boat, an' I'll go to court!"

"Mike, you're makin' it real hard. I don't see how —" Jabe was lost in doubt. Suddenly, he brightened. "Mebbe I kin run a boat on dry land."

He jumped awkwardly to the shore and made his way up the hill. Soon he returned with a long coupled wagon. The heavy wagon, with four oxen, lumbered down Third Street. A yawl was loaded on the wagon. Then Mike and his boatmen crawled into the yawl. They had their long poles with them. Mike took his place in the stern, and they looked all ready to shove off in the Ohio's current.

It had been raining most of the morning, but the rain had almost stopped when the load began to move. The road was muddy and slippery.

"Hi up! Ho! Ho!" the drivers cried. The sharp hooves of the four oxen skidded and slid and then dug into the mud as the drivers urged them up the steep hill.

The crowd grew larger and lined both sides of the street. They laughed and shouted. Certainly no one had ever seen such a way to take a person to court. The new constable was a great success.

The oxen advanced up the hill slowly. The soft mud gave them a poor footing. Their feet slipped aside or back. Often they stumbled and fell to their knees. But they lowered their heads, leaned earnestly into their yokes and made slow but steady progress up the hill.

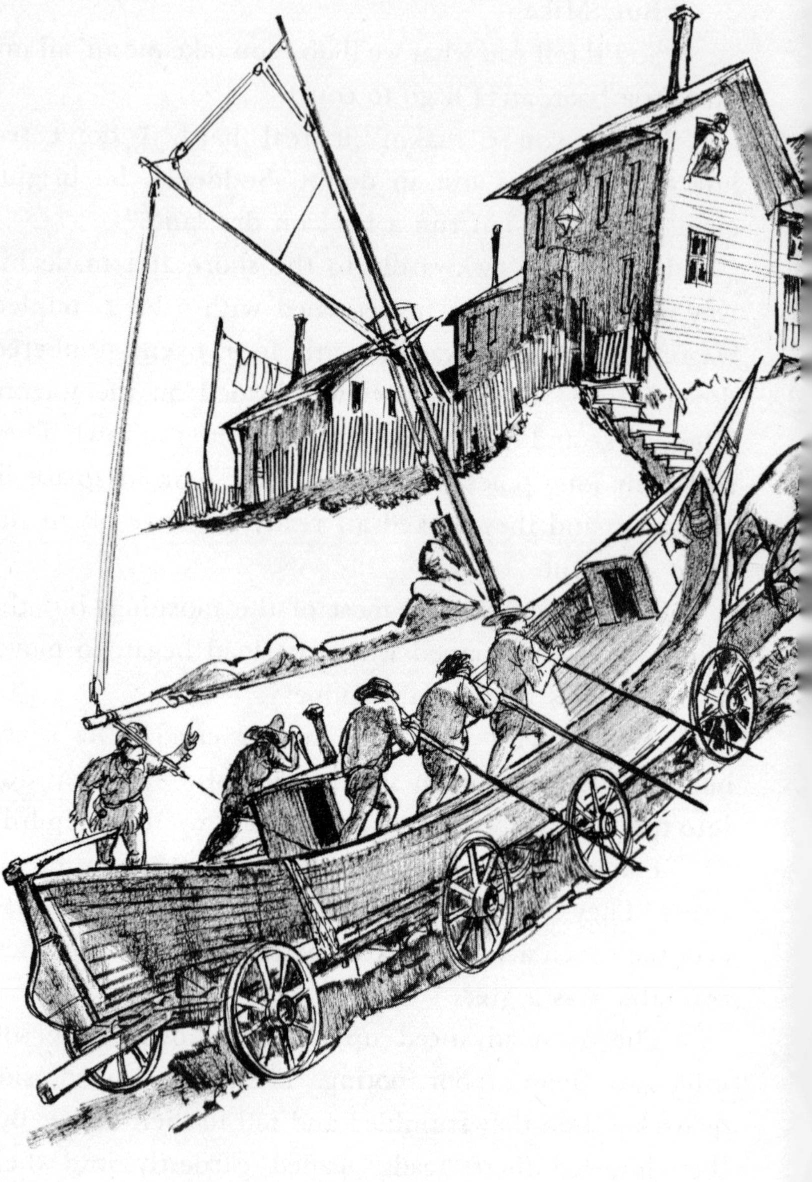

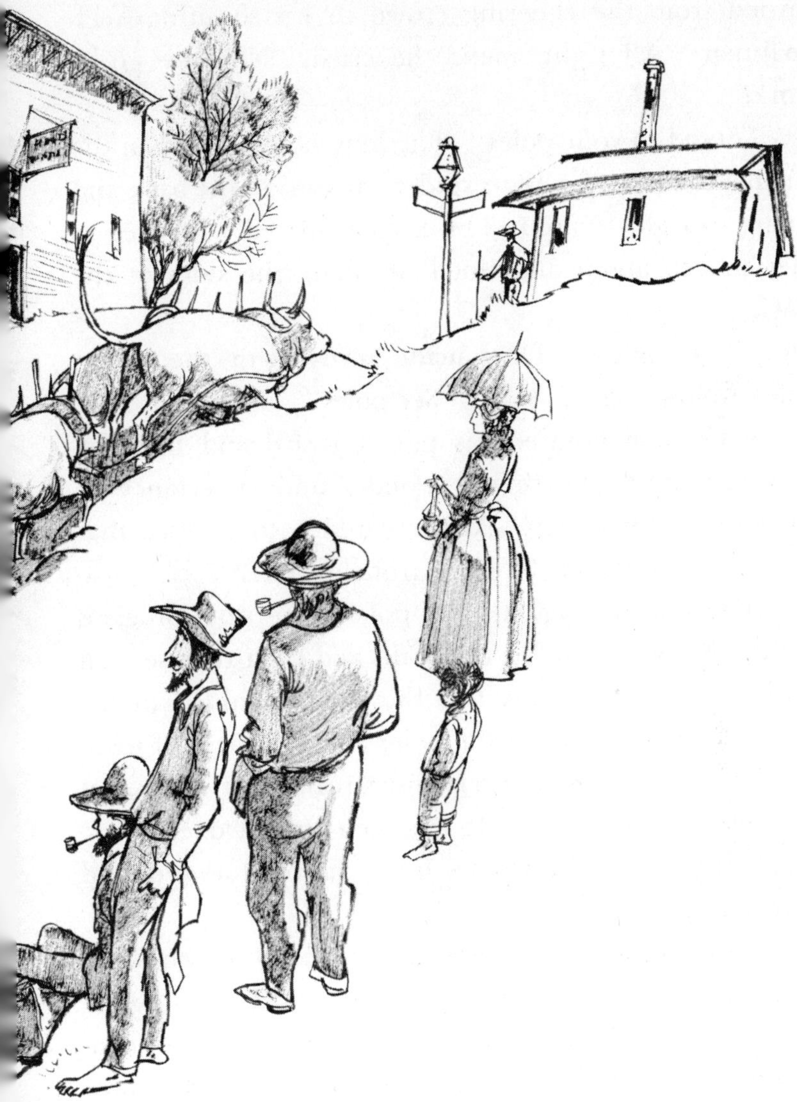

When they approached the halfway mark, Mike turned from the cheering crowd to his shouting keelboatmen. "All right, men," he cried. "Now we go to work!"

"Stand to your poles!" The long poles moved in the air like the legs of a giant spider thrown on his back and trying to right himself. The keelers roared with glee as they moved about and lined up along the sides of the yawl.

"Toss poles!" They made ready with their long poles. "Now," cried Mike. "Set poles!"

Each man pointed his pole forward and into the Kentucky mud. There was wonder and expectancy in the crowd. "Back her!" Mike roared with a voice that made the boards on the store fronts quiver.

The men lay against the poles. The slow progress of the oxen was brought to a halt, and then reversed. In a scramble of struggling feet the oxen stumbled in the mud against the force of the poles and the backs of men.

This was like going fernenst stream. But it was not men against the current. It was men against oxen.

"Head two!" Two poles lifted, moved forward, and were set again.

"Up behind!" Two more poles moved forward and were set.

"Up behind!" The commands came fast. The men, who had spent their lives pushing against the river, now spent a few uproarious minutes pushing against the oxen.

"Down on her!" Backs strained. Poles bent. The

Mike Fink's Trip to Court

oxen were not equal to the task. Their sixteen feet beat erratic tattoos in the wet, slippery earth, and they were dragged back down the hill.

The patroon's commands came again, like the crack of a rifle. The audience cheered. The keelers roared. The oxen bellowed and stumbled. Shouts and laughter filled the air. And down to the bottom of the hill went wagon, yawl, men and oxen.

Jabe Knuckles clambered down the hill after them. His proud march toward the court house had become a wild retreat. His boots struck the mud and a spray of soft, brown goo flowered out at every stride.

He caught up with the strangely loaded wagon, out of breath. "What's the trouble? What's wrong, Mike?" he asked anxiously.

"I don't know if I ought to go to court," Mike said.

"But, Mike, you got to. I mean, please do," Jabe pleaded.

"I never had much experience with courts," Mike said. "Mebbe I won't like it."

"It won't hurt you," said Jabe plaintively. "If you don't go I'll lose my job sure. You remember you won the case where the judge said a yeller-bellied catfish sank your Kentucky boat."

"Oh, well," said Mike. "I might as well — fer a friend." He turned to his men. "Poles up!" he commanded. The poles obediently rose. "Let 'er go with the current!"

"Hi up! Ho! Ho!" the drivers shouted again. They cracked their whips. The oxen lowered their heads and dug in. The heavy load once more started up the hill. It almost got to the top when once more Mike raised his voice. "Stand to your poles!"

"Toss poles!"

"Set poles!" he commanded. The long poles were pushed into the mud.

"Back her!" Once more the oxen slipped and slid, scrambled and stumbled, and gave ground to the men with the long poles, who had the strength of oxen.

Once more the people laughed and cheered. Once more the boatmen roared. Once more there was a parley at the foot of the muddy hill. And once more the strange craft made its way to court. It was more fun than a husking bee. It was more fun than a coon hunt. It was more fun than a medicine show, or a fight, or roof raising. It was more fun!

In court at last, Mike stood with Bang All in his hands, waiting for his accusers. He fingered his rifle. But no accuser came forward. The judge called for an accusation. There was none. He turned to Mike. "You are dismissed," he said. "I'm sorry fer the trouble caused you. An' I'm real glad the king of the boatmen came to my court. On land or on the river, you're a great man. Some day, Louisville will no doubt raise a monument in your honor."

"T'warn't no trouble at all," said Mike. He went out of the court and boarded the strange land-going craft. His men scrambled in after him. With the commands of a patroon, the strong oxen were once more pulled unwillingly through the greasy, gravy-like mud to the bottom of the hill.

15. To the Western Rivers

THE *Lightfoot* put out into the river. She dropped down the Falls of the Ohio. They passed Shawneetown and Cave-in-Rock. They swirled into the Mississippi and worked their way up toward St. Louis.

They were a day away from St. Louis. A big river steamer drew up to them one morning as they were pushing off.

"Let's give that smoke-belchin', steam-spittin', wood-burnin' divil a race," said Mike.

"Sure," Carpenter cried.

"Race her to St. Looie," shouted Talbott.

"Let's go!"

"We'll show her!"

The crew sprang to their oars. The *Lightfoot* pushed

the water aside into small foam-topped waves. The men were fresh. She drew ahead of the steamer. But the big, smoking craft caught up and slowly passed the keelboat. Passengers and crew gathered along the rail and looked down at the toiling men on the keelboat.

"Hitch a span of catfish on her!" one shouted.

"Better git an engine!" another cried.

The morning wore on. "Never mind, boys. She'll break down," Mike said. "They always do," he added scornfully. "There! See! She's headin' fer shore!"

A cheer went up.

No. She hadn't broken down. It wasn't that. She needed wood and stopped to take on fuel. The *Lightfoot* sped ahead again.

"We're doin' fine, boys, fine," Mike said gaily.

They were ahead when they heard two whistle blasts far back of them. The steamer was starting once more. The keelboatmen worked harder still.

They heard a long wavering blast as the big craft pulled around the bend back of them. It sounded like an angry threat. St. Louis was in sight. They had a chance to win. Just a chance, for the big boat was coming fast.

The sun was falling fast. The day was almost gone. The captain of the steamer had to win. He had ordered full steam ahead. The engineer could not fail. If the big, proud steamer lost to a little old keelboat, neither the captain nor the engineer could face the jeers of St. Louis. They knew that. And now pine pitch was being thrown into the flaming furnaces. The magic of fire and water created steam, and steam gave birth to power and power pushed the monstrous boat forward.

The keelers saw the flames from the pine pitch surge from the stacks, stabbing through billowing clouds of black smoke. They were tired. Weary to the point of exhaustion. The reserves of their own strength arose. The unknown and untried power that had been built into the bone and the flesh of Mike Fink and his men came into their arms and hearts. It was more than physical strength. It was courage, too, and heart. It had been built in them through days and years on the rivers, on the trails, in the woods.

The oars bent. The *Lightfoot* turned toward the St. Louis landing.

"She'll bust down! She'll blow a gasket! She'll strip a gear!" Mike half shouted and half prayed.

But she did none of those things. She flowed ahead. The boatmen heard the jeers and they heard the cheers. A long agonizing shriek of the steamer's whistle drowned out these sounds. The big boat turned toward the landing, too. Her wash tossed the *Lightfoot*. Her black smoke swept down and covered the keelboat. The big steam-powered craft made the landing first.

Mike had lost the race. A man with a pole was no match for the power of steam. But his friends had seen the brave finish and Mike was still a hero. Always would be. A person who loses a race, somehow in a way, wins — if he runs a good race.

Mike delivered his freight and the *Lightfoot* stood empty. Waiting for another load. Up the river. Down

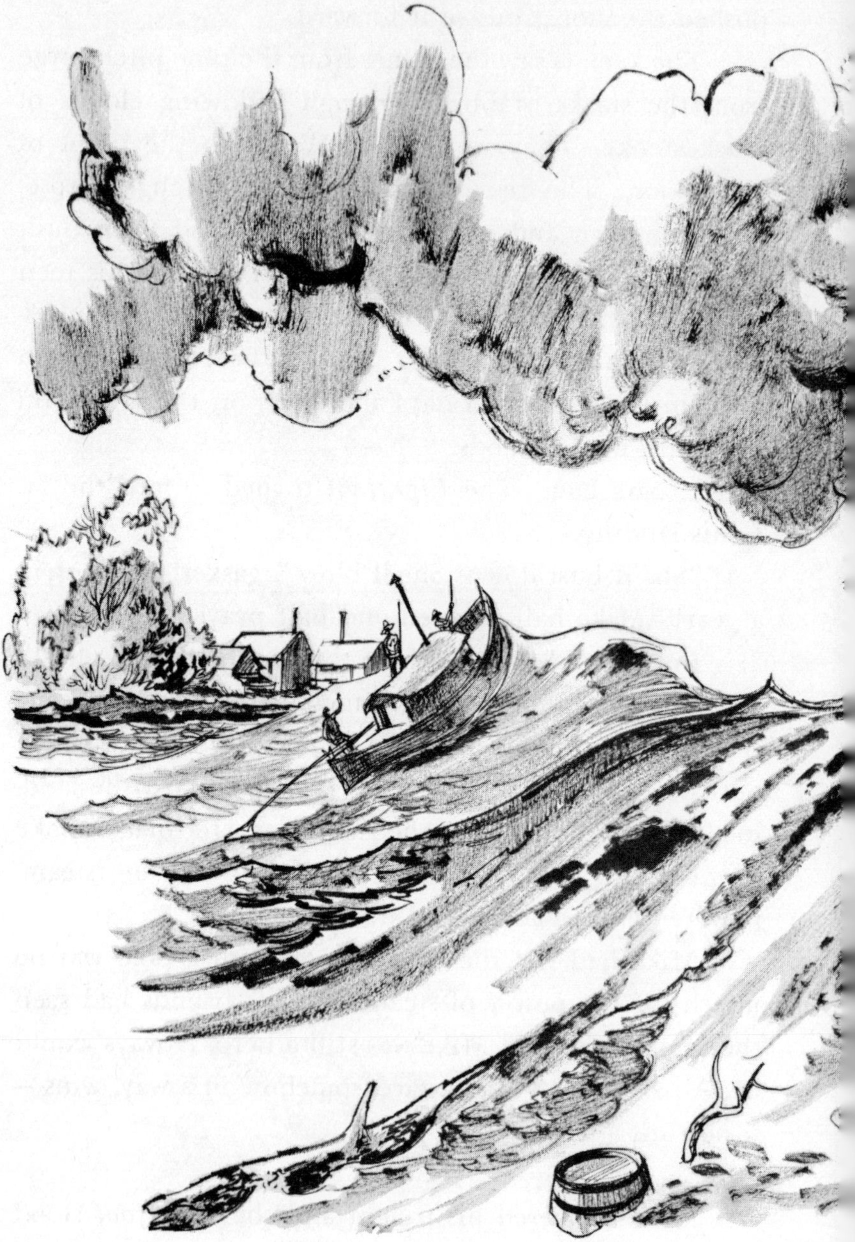

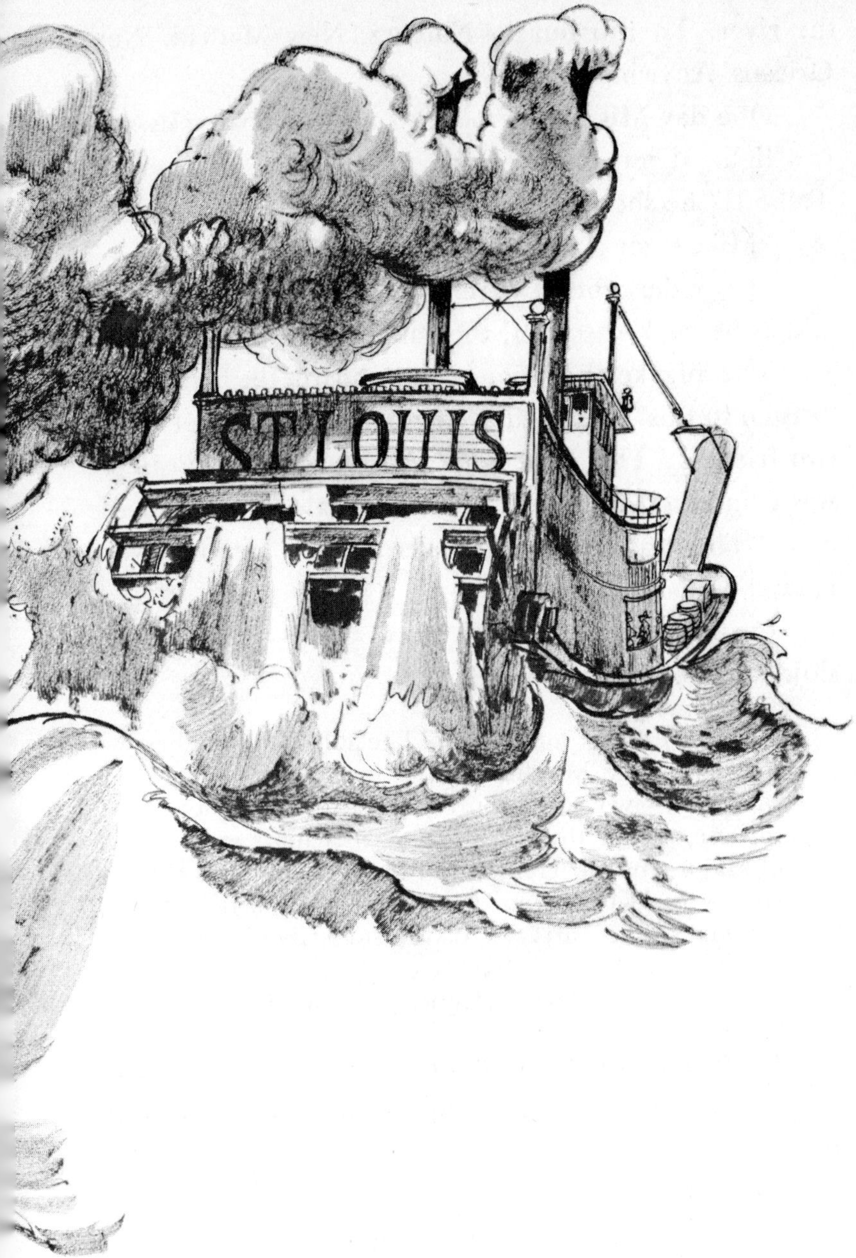
ST LOUIS

the river. To Pittsburgh, Natchez, New Madrid, New Orleans. Anywhere.

One day Mike came back to the keelboat. His step was light. There was a shine in his eyes. "Carpenter! Talbott!" he shouted.

"Mike's got a load," said Talbott.

"I wonder where we're goin' this time," Carpenter said as he walked toward the gangplank.

The big keelboatman came aboard the *Lightfoot*. "Listen to this!" he cried as he waved a newspaper at his two friends. "This here is the *Missoury Republican*. It was printed on March 22, 1822," he said as he read the date. "That was day before yesterday. Jest listen to what it says!"

Carpenter and Talbott drew close as Mike Fink slowly spelled out the words.

>*To enterprising young men.* The subscriber wishes to engage one hundred young men to ascend the Missouri River to its source, there to be employed for one, two or three years. For particulars enquire of Major Andrew Henry, near the lead mines in the county of Washington, who will ascend with, and command, the party; or of the subscriber near St. Louis.
>
>[Signed] William H. Ashley.

Carpenter drew his breath. "You goin'?" he asked.

"You're all-fired tarnation tootin', I am!" Mike replied.

"But, Mike — "

"This part of the country is gettin' too tame. Too civilized," Mike Fink declared. "They ain't no mean

Injuns. No river pirates. No renegades. Nothin'! Look at me! I'm dreadful disgusted. For want of real, first-rate, he-man excitement, I start snitchin' sheep. Tame sheep at that!"

"It was his comeuppance. Anyway, it's over now."

"Sure 'nuf, it's over. Look. I'm gettin' soft. I bin whipped recently. Not by a real man. Not with fists, or with a gun. Not by the wilderness. But by nothin' more than a brindle bull, a couple of yaller houn' dogs an' some wasps!" He shrugged his shoulders and sighed deeply with despair. "An' by a smokin', steamin', wood-chawin' critter that ain't got hide nor hair, nor bones, nor tallow, nor muscle — nor brains!" he added.

"But mebbe — "

"No mebbe to it. It ain't no good. None of it. An' then, to top it all off, I'm hauled to court by some big, dumb oxen that ain't even able to take me to court if I don't want 'em to."

"But, Mike. Jest think — "

"Yep. Jest think!" he exclaimed. "I knew all this country before a squatter's axe had blazed a tree. Whoever shot bear by building a log cabin? There ain't no excitement any more. Only signs of civilization, instead of Injun sign. I'm goin' to git out of here quicker than lightnin' kin run down a cypress."

"There's a lot in what you say. Why, I remember — "

" 'Course there is. An' now there is the steamboats. Huffin' an' puffin' like the breath of all the creeturs in creation was smokin' through a stovepipe. Though I doubt they will ever be successful, they do go fernenst stream without a man at a pole — "

"An' no cordelle neither," said Carpenter.

"Or oars," Talbott added.

"Them steamboats ain't fer me. They're too easy. War, famine an' bloodshed puts flesh on my bones, an' hardship is my daily bread."

"Mike, I thought your life was here on the river, but mebbe it ain't."

"'Course it ain't, mannee. I used to be as happy here on the river as a mud turkle in a puddle. But then it was the frontier. In front of the frontier even. It ain't the real frontier no more. The frontier is farther west.

"It's so tame I jest can't stand it. That's the reason I'm goin' with Ashley. To the Rockies. To Three Forks. To the head waters of the Missoury. To the Great Divide. To the Pacific! Where the bars is grizzly bars, an' big enough to give a man a fight. Where Injuns wear their war paint fer breakfast! An' where beaver grows so numerous that wealth awaits, greater than all the silver mines of Peru!"

Carpenter said suddenly, "You're right! An' I'm goin' with you!"

"Me, too," said Talbott.

"Good boy! Good boy!" said Mike. "You're more than welcome!"

Mike turned his leather-colored face to the west. A face tanned and hardened by sun and wind and storm. "I kind of hate to leave the ole Ohio and the Massassip. There's still some fight, some gumption in 'em."

To the Western Rivers

His eyes lit up. "But then there's other rivers out west," he said.

And Mike did go west. In the company of "enterprising young men" were men who could fight. And there was plenty to fight. Indians, renegades, wild animals, wild country, and wild rivers. It was a crew that left its mark. And what a mark! The whole, great, endless, wild west.

In Ashley's crew were names that have filled a long shelf of history books. Names that have made a thousand tales. Jedediah Strong Smith, Jim Bridger, Hugh Glass, to name a few. And, to name one — Mike Fink, the best of the keelboatmen.

The Author

HAROLD W. FELTON, a lawyer by profession, has for many years devoted his leisure time to writing for young people. An intense interest in American folklore led to the first of his widely acclaimed books, an anthology of legends about Paul Bunyan. Since that time he has pursued folk heroes and tall tales with enthusiasm, and his *Pecos Bill: Texas Cowpuncher; John Henry and His Hammer; Fire-Fightin' Mose; Bowleg Bill: Seagoing Cowpuncher; Cowboy Jamboree;* and *New Tall Tales of Pecos Bill* rank him as a master yarn-spinner.

Born in the Midwest, Mr. Felton now lives in Jackson Heights, New York.

The Artist

ALDREN A. WATSON, whose inimitable drawings depict the heroic-comic adventures of the legendary yet very real Mike Fink, is well known as an illustrator of books for children and young people. His versatility is reflected in numerous titles, including the charming picture books by his wife, Nancy Dingman Watson, and previous titles by Harold Felton. Mr. Watson and his family reside in Putney, Vermont.

BURLINGTON TOWNSHIP HIGH SCHOOL LIBRARY